730 Daily Math Warm-ups

Hope Martin

J. WESTON

WALCH
PUBLISHER

Portland, Maine

1   2   3   4   5   6   7   8   9   10

ISBN 0-8251-2802-1

Copyright © 1996
J. Weston Walch, Publisher
P. O. Box 658 • Portland, Maine 04104-0658

Printed in the United States of America

To the Teacher

Have you found, as a middle school teacher, that you never seem to have enough time to get to all of the interesting and exciting mathematics you would like? Imagine having just five minutes more each day. For 180 teaching days, that would give you 900 more minutes of mathematics each year. This adds up to about *22 more teaching periods* a year, or an *extra month* of valuable teaching time. You can get this extra time—not by lengthening the period, but by really *using* the first five minutes, the most crucial minutes of the class period. The activities presented in *730 Daily Math Warm-ups* will supply you with interesting and mathematically enriching puzzles to get your students thinking about mathematics from the *minute* they enter class. If you convert these blackline masters into transparencies and place them on the overhead, your students will have the opportunity to use deductive reasoning skills on mathematically challenging puzzles while they are learning about historical events.

The National Council of Teachers of Mathematics *Curriculum and Evaluation Standards for School Mathematics* describes the 5–8 curriculum as having the following features:

- Problem situations that establish the need for new ideas and motivate students should serve as the context for mathematics . . . (p. 66)

- A balance should be struck between problems that apply to mathematics in the real world and problems that arise from the investigation of mathematical ideas. (p. 75)

- Reasoning is fundamental to the knowing and doing of mathematics. To give students access to mathematics as a powerful way of making sense of the world, it is essential that an emphasis on reasoning pervade all mathematical activity. (p. 81)

- For many students, mathematics in the middle grades has far too often simply repeated or extended much of the computational work covered in earlier grades. . . Students should have many opportunities to observe the interaction of mathematics with other school subjects and with everyday society. (p. 84)

- The mathematics curriculum should include the study of number systems and number theory so that students can develop and apply number theory concepts (e.g., primes, factors, and multiples) in real-world and mathematical situations. (p. 91)

With the spirit and philosophy of the *Standards* as my guide, I have designed the puzzles contained in *730 Daily Math Warm-ups* to make the connection for your students between the mathematics classroom and the real world. Mathematical concepts have not been sequenced; they are to be learned within the context of the problem.

The daily puzzles contained in *730 Daily Math Warm-ups* will give your students the opportunity to explore:

- whole numbers and whole number algorithms

- place value

- rational numbers (fractions, decimals, and percents)

- exponents and square roots

- area and perimeter

- rules of divisibility

- primes and composite numbers

- odd and even numbers

- factors and perfect numbers

- triangular and square numbers

- other figurate numbers (pentagonal, hexagonal, etc.)

- number patterns such as palindromes

- factorials

- greatest common factor and least common multiple

- Fibonacci's sequence

As they solve these daily puzzles, your students will be using context clues to solve problems, will intuitively interpret quantitative clues, and will connect the abstract rules of number theory to an interesting and fun activity. As students find the "sum of consecutive integers" as well as other imponderables in these puzzles, they gain confidence in their problem-solving abilities and become better problem solvers.

Two puzzles are supplied for every day of the year. Puzzles assigned for homework can be solved by parents and students working together. I wish you a year of fruitful and exciting mathematics.

— Hope Martin

Glossary of Terms

abundant number   A natural number that is less than the sum of its proper divisors—that is, all of its natural number divisors except the number itself.
Example: 12 is an abundant number because $1 + 2 + 3 + 4 + 6 = 16$ and $16 > 12$.
The next abundant number is 18 because $1 + 2 + 3 + 6 + 9 = 21$ and $21 > 18$.

area   The number of square units needed to cover a surface. The area of a rectangle is found by multiplying the length by the width.

average   The measure of central tendency that is found by finding the sum and dividing by the number of terms.

base   The number used as the factor: in 2^3, 2 is the base.

composite number   A natural number that has more than two factors.

consecutive integers   A series of two or more integers that become one greater than the preceding integer, e.g., 7, 8, 9 are three consecutive integers.

deficient numbers   A natural number that is greater than the sum of its proper divisors—that is, all of its natural number divisors except the number itself.
Example: 4 is a deficient number because $1 + 2 = 3$ and $3 < 4$; 10 is a deficient number because $1 + 2 + 5 = 8$ and $8 < 10$. There are many deficient numbers.

divisible   A number is divisible by another if the quotient is a whole number and the remainder is zero.

factor   When two or more numbers are multiplied, each number is a factor of the product. The factors of 48 are 1, 2, 3, 4, 6, 8, 12, 16, 24, 48.

factorial   The product of a given series of consecutive whole numbers beginning with 1 and ending with the number.
$$0! = 1$$
$$1! = 1 \times 1 = 1$$
$$2! = 2 \times 1 = 2$$
$$3! = 3 \times 2 \times 1 = 6$$
$$4! = 4 \times 3 \times 2 \times 1 = 24$$
$$5! = 5 \times 4 \times 3 \times 2 \times 1 = 120$$
$$6! = 6 \times 5 \times 4 \times 3 \times 2 \times 1 = 720$$
$$n! = n \times (n-1) \times (n-2) \times (n-3) \dots \times 1$$

Fibonacci numbers   An infinite series of natural numbers in which each term is the sum of the preceding two terms, example: 1, 1, 2, 3, 5, 8, 13, 21. . .

figurate numbers   Numbers that can be used to represent geometric figures.
Triangular numbers: 1, 3, 6, 10, 15, 21 . . . $\frac{n(n+1)}{2}$, where n is the term of the sequence

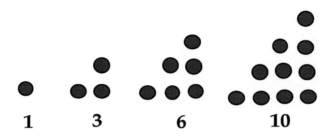

Square numbers: 1, 4, 9, 16, 25, . . . n^2, where n is the term of the sequence

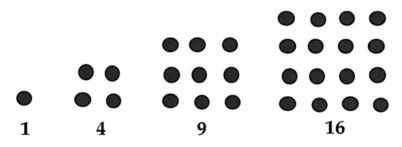

palindrome   A natural number of two or more digits that is the same whether it is read forwards or backwards, example: 44, 121, 1331, 1234321.

Pascal's triangle   An infinite triangle that begins with one at the peak; each successive row is produced by taking the sum of the two contiguous numbers in the preceding row,

1

1 1

1 2 1

1 3 3 1

1 4 6 4 1

1 5 10 10 5 1

1 6 15 20 15 6 1

730 Daily Math Warm-ups

perfect number   A natural number that equals the sum of its proper divisors—that is, all of its whole number divisors except the number itself.

Example: 6 is a perfect number because $1 + 2 + 3 = 6$
28 is a perfect number because $1 + 2 + 4 + 7 + 14 = 28$
The next two perfect numbers are 496 and 8,128.

prime number   Any natural number greater than one that has two and only two factors. The prime numbers less than 100 are 2, 3, 5, 7, 11, 13, 17, 19, 23, 29, 31, 37, 41, 43, 47, 53, 59, 61, 67, 71, 73, 79, 83, 89, 97.

rules of divisibility   A number is divisible by:

2:   if the units digit is 0, 2, 4, 6, or 8; if it is an even number
3:   if the sum of the digits of the number is divisible by 3
4:   if the last two digits of the number are divisible by 4
5:   if the last digit of the number is 0 or 5
6:   if the number is an even number and is divisible by 3
8:   if the last three digits of the number are divisible by 8
9:   if the sum of the digits of the number is divisible by 9
10:   if the last digit of the number is 0

scientific notation   A way of writing a number as a product of two factors; the first factor is at least 1 but less than 10 and the second factor is the necessary power of 10.
Example: $5,700 = 5.7 \times 10^3$. The advantage of using scientific notation is that the size and precision of numbers can easily be compared; the first number shows the precision and the second shows the size. It is also very helpful when reading very large or very small numbers.

volume   The number of cubic units necessary to fill a three-dimensional space. The volume of a cube $= s^3$.

January 1

On January 1 of this year, American patriot Paul Revere was born in Boston, Massachusetts. He is best known through Longfellow's poem "The Midnight Ride of Paul Revere."

- My tens and units digits are twin primes whose sum is equal to the sum of my thousands and hundreds digit.
- The sum of my digits is 16.
- My date is divisible by 5.

What year am I?

On January 1 of this year, American flag-maker Betsy Ross was born in Philadelphia, Pennsylvania. Legend tells us that she created the first Stars and Stripes under the direction of George Washington.

- Both my tens and units digits are prime numbers, but my tens is odd and my units is even.
- The sum formed by adding my tens and units digits is a multiple of my hundreds digit.
- The sum of all of my digits is 15.

What year am I?

January 2

On January 2 of this year, the first junior high school was opened in the United States.

- My thousands and tens digits could be the sides of a square with an area of only 1 square unit.
- My hundreds digit is equal to 3^2.
- The sum of all of my digits is only 11.

What year am I?

On January 2 of this year, Russian-American science fiction writer and scientist Isaac Asimov was born.

- My tens digit is the only even prime number.
- My date is divisible by 2, 3, 4, 5, 6, and 12.
- The sum of all of my digits is 12.

What year am I?

January 3

On January 3 of this year, author J.R.R. Tolkien was born in South Africa. His best-known work is *The Hobbit* of *The Lord of the Rings* trilogy.

- My units digit is 25% of my even hundreds digit.
- My hundreds and tens digits are consecutive integers with a product of 72.
- The sum of all of my digits is 20.

What year am I?

On January 3 of this year, Russian-born mathematician Sonya Kovalevskaya was born.

- My date is divisible by 2, 5, and 10.
- My prime tens digit is three less than my cubic hundreds digit.
- The sum of my digits is 14.

What year am I?

January 4

On January 4 of this year, folklorist and grammarian Jacob Grimm was born in Hanau, Germany. He is best known for *Grimm's Fairy Tales*, which he collected with his brother, Wilhelm.

- My hundreds and tens digits are consecutive integers whose product is 56.
- The sum of my thousands and hundreds digit is equal to my tens digit.
- My units digit is the third prime number.

What year am I?

On January 4 of this year, Louis Braille was born in France. He invented the raised-point method of writing for the blind. At the age of 3, he was blinded by an accident. He developed a system of writing using a stylus to punch holes in paper that could be felt by the blind.

- The sum of my thousands and hundreds digits is equal to my units digit.
- My units digit is equal to 3^2.
- The sum of my digits is 18.

What year am I?

January 5

On January 5 of this year, German physicist Wilhelm Roentgen announced the discovery of the X ray.

- If my hundreds and tens digits were the sides of a rectangle, it would have a perimeter of 34 and an area of 72.
- My date is a multiple of 5.
- The sum of all of my digits is 23.

What year am I?

On January 5 of this year, Nellie Tayloe Ross took the oath of office as the first female governor in the United States. The state was Wyoming.

- The product of my tens and units digits is equal to the sum of my hundreds and thousand digits.
- My tens and units digits are prime numbers, although the tens is even and the units is odd.
- The two-digit number formed by my tens and units digits could be the area of a square.

What year am I?

January 6

On January 6 of this year, French saint and national heroine Joan of Arc was born.

- The two-digit number formed by my thousands and hundreds digits is two greater than the two-digit number formed by my tens and units digits.
- Both of these two-digit numbers are divisible by 2; but the number formed by the thousands and hundreds digits is also divisible by 7, while the number formed by the tens and units digits is divisible by 3, 4, and 6.
- The sum of all of my digits is only 8.

What year am I?

On January 6 of this year, President Franklin Delano Roosevelt delivered his "Four Freedoms" speech: freedom from want, freedom from fear, freedom of religion, and freedom of speech and expression.

- If my hundreds and tens digits were the sides of a rectangle, its area would be 36 and its perimeter would be 26.
- Both my thousands and units digits are the multiplicative identity.
- If my tens digit were five greater, my date would be a palindrome.

What year am I?

January 7

On January 7 of this year, the first presidential election was held in the United States.

- My hundreds, tens, and units digits are consecutive integers whose mean is 8.
- The sum of my digits is 25.

   What year am I?

On January 7 of this year, the Panama Canal was opened to traffic. The first boat to cross "the path between the seas" was the crane boat *Alex La Valley*. It wasn't until August 3 that an oceangoing vessel passed through the canal, which connects the Atlantic and Pacific oceans.

- The sum of my thousands and hundreds digits is equal to twice the sum of my tens and units digits.
- My thousands and tens digits are the same odd number.
- Both my hundreds and tens digits are square numbers.

   What year am I?

January 8

On January 8 of this year, American rock-and-roll singer Elvis Aaron Presley was born in Tupelo, Mississippi.

- My tens and units digits are consecutive prime integers whose sum is one less than my hundreds digit.
- My date is divisible by 3, 5, and 9.
- My tens digit is $\frac{1}{3}$ of my hundreds digit.

   What year am I?

On January 8 of this year, comedian Soupy Sales (Morton Supman) was born in Wake Forest, North Carolina.

- The square root of my hundreds digit is equal to my tens digit.
- The sum of my digits is 13.

   What year am I?

January 9

On January 9 of this year, Frenchman François Jean Pierre Blanchard traveled between Philadelphia and New Jersey in the first successful balloon flight in the United States. The balloon reached a height of over 5,800 feet and traveled 15 miles in 45 minutes. (How many miles per hour is this?)

- My units digit squared is equal to my tens digit; both of them are odd numbers.
- The sum of my thousands digit and my prime hundreds digit is one less than my tens digit.

What year am I?

On January 9 of this year, New York City Ballet Company founder George Balanchine was born in St. Petersburg, Russia. He choreographed more than 200 ballets, including *Swan Lake*.

- Both my hundreds and my units digits are square numbers, but one is odd and the other is even.
- My date is divisible by 2 and 4.
- My tens digit is the additive identity element.
- The sum of all of my digits is 14.

What year am I?

January 10

On January 10 of this year, Ethan Allen was born in Litchfield, Connecticut. He was the leader of the Green Mountain Boys and a hero of the American Revolution.

- My units digit is equal to $\sqrt{64}$; my tens digit is equal to $\sqrt{9}$.
- The sum of my hundreds digits and 1 is equal to my units digit.

What year am I?

On January 10 of this year, the League of Nations was established. This predecessor of the United Nations was dissolved 26 years after it was formed. The United States never joined the League.

- If a decimal point were placed in front of the two-digit number formed by my tens and units digits, it would be equivalent to the fraction $\frac{1}{5}$.
- My date is divisible by 2, 3, 5, and 6.
- The sum of 1 and my tens digit is $33\frac{1}{3}\%$ of my hundreds digit.

What year am I?

January 11

On January 11 of this year, Chicago schools were closed in the wake of the record-breaking –26°F temperatures.

- My units digit raised to the third power is equal to my tens digit.
- My hundreds digit minus my thousands digit is equal to my tens digit.

What year am I?

On January 11 of this year, American statesman Alexander Hamilton was born in the British West Indies. He was mortally wounded in a duel with Aaron Burr.

- My hundreds, tens, and units digits form a palindrome; all of the digits are prime and odd.
- If my hundreds and units digits were the sides of a square, its area would be 49.
- The sum of all of my digits is 20.

What year am I?

January 12

On January 12 of this year, American adventure writer Jack London was born in San Francisco. Among his more than 50 books of outdoor adventures was *The Call of the Wild*.

- My hundreds, tens, and units digits are consecutive integers whose mean is 7.
- My date is divisible by 2 and 4.
- The sum of all of my digits is 22.

What year am I?

On January 12 of this year, voters elected the first woman U.S. senator: Hattie Caraway from the state of Arkansas.

- My tens digit raised to the power of my units digit is equal to my hundreds digit.
- The sum of my thousands and units digits is equal to my tens digit.
- The sum of all of my digits is 15.

What year am I?

January 13

On January 13 of this year, Robert C. Weaver became the first black cabinet member when he was appointed Secretary of Housing and Urban Development by President Lyndon B. Johnson.

- My tens and units digits are the same even number; each has a value equal to 3!.
- The sum of my digits is 22.

What year am I?

On January 13 of this year, the accordion was patented. This is a musical instrument with keys, metal reeds, and bellows. By fingering the keys, air is forced through the reeds by opening and closing the bellows.

- The two-digit number formed by my tens and units digits is divisible by 2, 3, 6, 9, 18, 27, 1, and itself.
- The sum of my thousands and hundreds digits is equal to the sum of my tens and units digits.

What year am I?

January 14

On January 14 of this year, Albert Schweitzer was born. The humanitarian missionary and physician spent most of his life in Africa helping its people.

- My tens and units digits are consecutive primes, but my units digit is two less than my tens digit.
- My hundreds digit is one more than my tens digit.
- My date is divisible by 3 and 5.

What year am I?

On January 14 of this year, the Pentagon building in Washington, D.C., was completed. It is the five-sided building that houses the Department of Defense.

- My hundreds and tens digits are square numbers, but one is odd and the other is even.
- The two-digit number formed by my tens and units digits is the 14th prime number.

What year am I?

January 15

On January 15 of this year, Martin Luther King, Jr., was born. Dr. King was America's most famous civil rights leader and received the Nobel Peace Prize for his important work.

- The two-digit number formed by my tens and units digits is prime and 10 greater than the two-digit number formed by my thousands and hundreds digits.
- The sum of my digits is 21.

What year am I?

On January 15 of this year, Hungarian-American physicist Edward Teller was born in Budapest.

- My units digit is one less than my hundreds digit; my tens digit is one less than my thousands digit.
- The sum of my digits is 18.

What year am I?

January 16

On January 16 of this year, the 18th Amendment became part of the U.S. Constitution. This amendment made the sale of alcoholic beverages illegal. This was the first time an amendment to the Constitution dealt with a social issue. The 18th Amendment was repealed by the 21st Amendment.

- My thousands and hundreds digits form the same two-digit number as my tens and units digits do.
- The sum of all of my digits is 20.

What year am I?

On January 16 of this year, the Allies launched a major offensive against Iraq; this was the beginning of the Persian Gulf War. The attack was broadcast live on TV by CNN News.

- My date is a palindrome.
- The sum of all of my digits is 20.

What year am I?

January 17

On January 17 of this year, Benjamin Franklin was born in Boston, Massachusetts. The American statesman, printer, scientist, and writer was the oldest signer of the Declaration of Independence.

- The sum of my perfect units digit and my thousands digit is equal to my hundreds digit.
- My tens digit is the additive identity.

What year am I?

On January 17 of this year, Englishman James Cook became the first explorer to cross the Antarctic Circle.

- My hundreds and tens digits could be the sides of a square with a perimeter of 28 and an area of 49.
- My date is divisible by both 3 and 9.
- The sum of all of my digits is 18.

What year am I?

January 18

On January 18 of this year, English author A. A. Milne was born in London, England. He is best known for the children's books *Winnie-the-Pooh* and *The House at Pooh Corner*.

- My hundreds and tens digits are the same cubic number.
- My units digit is equal to $\sqrt[3]{8}$.
- The sum of all of my digits is 19.

What year am I?

On January 18 of this year, Peter Roget was born in London, England. He wrote *Roget's Thesaurus of English Words and Phrases*.

- My hundreds and tens digits are the same prime number.
- My units digit is two more than my tens digit.
- The sum of all of my digits is 24.

What year am I?

January 19

On January 19 of this year, Confederate general Robert E. Lee was born in Stratford, Virginia. His birth date is observed in Arkansas, Georgia, Louisiana, South Carolina, and Texas.

- My prime units digit plus my thousands digit is equal to my even hundreds digit.
- The product of my tens digit and any other number is equal to my tens digit.
- The sum of all of my digits is 16.

What year am I?

On January 19 of this year, the world's record snowfall fell on London, England. Drifts of 4.5 meters were measured. (How many feet is 4.5 meters?)

- My date is a palindrome with a sum of 18.

What year am I?

January 20

On January 20 of this year, the United States Medicare Bill was signed into law. It gave medical insurance to older Americans.

- My tens and units digits could be the sides of a square.
- My tens digit is $66\frac{2}{3}\%$ of my hundreds digit.
- The sum of my digits is 22.

What year am I?

On January 20 of this year, comedian and actor George Burns (Nathan Birnbaum) was born in New York City. He costarred with his wife in the *George Burns and Gracie Allen Show* and later appeared in the movie *Oh God*.

- My units digit is $\frac{3}{4}$ of my hundreds digit but only $\frac{2}{3}$ of my tens digit.
- My date is divisible by 2, 3, 4, and 6.
- My units digit is a perfect number.

What year am I?

 730 Daily Math Warm-ups

January 21

On January 21 of this year, the first law requiring that drivers of automobiles have licenses went into effect.

- My prime tens and units digits could be the sides of a rectangle with a perimeter of 20 and an area of 21.
- The two-digit number formed by my tens and units digits is the 12th prime number.
- My tens digit raised to the second power is equal to my hundreds digit.

What year am I?

On January 21 of this year, Barney Clark was born in Provo, Utah. He was the first person to receive a permanent artificial heart. The heart was made of plastic and aluminum. Although he lived only 112 days following the 1983 operation, Clark helped pave the way for some of the medical advances of today.

- The sum of my digits is only 13.
- The two-digit number formed by my tens and units digits is divisible by 3 and 7.
- Three times the sum of my tens and units digits is equal to my hundreds digit.

What year am I?

January 22

On January 22 of this year, former Secretary General of the United Nations U Thant was born.

- The sum of the two-digit number formed by my thousands and hundreds digits is one greater than my units digit.
- My hundreds and units digits are the same square number.
- The sum of all of my digits is 19.

What year am I?

On January 22 of this year, American author Joseph Wambaugh was born. He is a former police detective.

- My tens digit is $33\frac{1}{3}\%$ of my hundreds digit.
- My units digit is the largest single-digit prime number.
- The sum of all of my digits is 20.

What year am I?

January 23

On January 23 of this year, Dr. Elizabeth Blackwell became the first woman to receive an M.D. degree. She received the degree from the Medical Institute of Geneva, New York.

- My tens digit is 50% of my hundreds digit.
- The sum of my thousands and hundreds digits is equal to my units digit.
- The sum of all of my digits is 22.

What year am I?

On January 23 of this year, John Hancock was born in Braintree, Massachusetts. He was the first signer of the Declaration of Independence; his name has become synonymous with the word "signature." (Have you ever heard the expression, "Put your John Hancock on that"?)

- My hundreds, tens, and units digits form a palindrome with a sum of 17.
- My tens and units digits could be the sides of a rectangle with a perimeter of 20 and an area of 21.

What year am I?

January 24

On January 24 of this year, a gold nugget was found at the site of a sawmill owned by John Sutter near Colona, California. This started the California Gold Rush.

- My even hundreds, tens, and units digits form a palindrome whose sum is 20.
- My hundreds digit is 200% of my tens digit.

What year am I?

On January 24 of this year, Native American ballerina Maria Tallchief was born.

- The two-digit number formed by my tens and units digits is equal to 5^2.
- The sum of my thousands and hundreds digits is equal to the product of my tens and units digits.

What year am I?

January 25

On January 25 of this year, Scottish poet Robert Burns was born in Alloway, Scotland. Burns wrote these words using the Scottish dialect: "Oh wad some power the giftie gie us to see oursels as others see us!"

- My hundreds, tens, and units digits are all odd numbers, but only the units digit is composite; the other two are prime.
- Two times my tens digit is equal to the sum of my thousands and units digits.
- The sum of all of my digits is 22.

What year am I?

On January 25 of this year, Felix Mendelssohn's newly composed "Wedding March" was played at the wedding of the Princess Royal.

- My hundreds and units digits could be the sides of a square with a perimeter of 32.
- My tens digit is equal to $\sqrt{25}$.
- The palindrome formed by my hundreds, tens, and units digits has a sum of 21.

What year am I?

January 26

On January 26 of this year, Benjamin Franklin expressed his unhappiness in a letter to his daughter over the choice of the eagle as the symbol of America. His choice would have been the turkey.

- My units digit is 50% of my tens digit.
- My tens digit is one more than my prime hundreds digit.
- The sum of all of my digits is 20.

What year am I?

On January 26 of this year, Michigan became the 26th state to be admitted to the United States.

- Both my tens and units digits are odd prime numbers; my units digit is four greater than my tens digit.
- The sum of my thousands and hundreds digits is three times the size of my tens digit.

What year am I?

January 27

On January 27 of this year, English author Lewis Carroll (Charles Lutwidge Dodgson) was born in Daresbury, England. He wrote *Alice in Wonderland*.

- The two-digit number formed by my tens and units digits could be the perimeter of a square with a side the size of my hundreds digit.
- My date is even.
- Three times my tens digit is equal to the sum of my hundreds and thousands digits.
- The sum of all of my digits is 14.

What year am I?

On January 27 of this year, composer Wolfgang Amadeus Mozart was born in Salzburg, Austria. He began performing at the age of 3 and composed his first piece at the age of 5. He died at the age of 35.

- My tens and units digits are consecutive integers whose sum is 11.
- My hundreds digit is the largest single-digit prime.
- My tens digit is two less than my hundreds digit.

What year am I?

January 28

On January 28 of this year, Louis Brandeis became the first American Jew to be appointed to the Supreme Court.

- The two-digit number formed by my tens and units digits is equal to 4^2.
- The two-digit number formed by my thousands and hundreds digits is the largest prime < 20.

What year am I?

On January 28 of this year, the world watched in horror as the space shuttle *Challenger* exploded 74 seconds into its flight. The seven people aboard the craft who died were teacher Christa McAuliffe and the six crew members—Francis Scobee, Michael Smith, Judith Resnick, Ellison Onizuka, Ronald McNair, and Gregory Jarvis.

- My date is divisible by 2, 3, and 6.
- My units digit is $66\frac{2}{3}\%$ of my hundreds digit but 75% of my tens digit.
- The sum of all of my digits is 24.

What year am I?

January 29

On January 29 of this year, Kansas was admitted to the United States as the 34th state.

- My tens digit is 75% of my hundreds digit.
- My thousands and units digits could be the sides of a square with a perimeter of 4.
- If my tens digit were two greater, my date would be a palindrome.

What year am I?

On January 29 of this year, baseball's American League was organized.

- My date, if written in scientific notation, would be 1.9×10^3.

What year am I?

January 30

On January 30 of this year, Franklin Delano Roosevelt was born in Hyde Park, New York. Roosevelt, the 32nd president of the United States, was elected to four presidential terms in office; he died during his fourth term. (The 22nd Amendment, limiting the number of terms a president could serve to two, was adopted in 1951.) Roosevelt said, "The only thing we have to fear is fear itself."

- My even units digit raised to the third power is equal to my tens digit.
- My hundreds digit and tens digit could be the sides of a square with an area of 64.
- The sum of all of my digits is 19.

What year am I?

On January 30 of this year, the first radio broadcast of *The Lone Ranger* was heard in the United States. The song played at the beginning of the program was the "William Tell Overture" from Rossini's opera. The program started and ended with the phrase "Heigh-ho, Silver."

- The product of my tens and units digits is equal to my hundreds digit.
- My tens and units digits could be the sides of a square with a perimeter of 12.

What year am I?

January 31

On January 31 of this year, the first daytime soap opera on television was broadcast from the NBC studios in Chicago. The show was *These Are My Children*.

- The square root of the two-digit number formed by my tens and units digits is 7.
- The sum of my digits is 23.

What year am I?

On January 31 of this year, composer Franz Schubert was born in Vienna, Austria. As he was dying, he requested that he be buried near the grave of Beethoven.

- My hundreds, tens, and units digits form a palindrome with a sum of 23.
- If my hundreds and tens digits were the sides of a rectangle its area would be 63 and its perimeter would be 32.

What year am I?

February 1

On February 1 of this year, the U. S. Supreme Court held its first session in the Royal Exchange Building in New York.

- My hundreds and tens digits are consecutive odd integers whose sum is 16.
- My date is divisible by both 5 and 10.

What year am I?

On February 1 of this year, Irish-American light-opera composer Victor Herbert was born in Dublin, Ireland.

- The sum of my hundreds and thousands digits is equal to my units digit.
- My tens digit is equal to $\sqrt{25}$.

What year am I?

February 2

On February 2 of this year, National Football League cofounder George Hallas was born in Chicago, Illinois. He owned and coached the Chicago Bears until shortly before his death.

- My date is divisible by 5 but not 10.
- My hundreds and tens digits are consecutive integers whose product is 72.
- My hundreds digit is cubic and my tens digit is square.

What year am I?

On February 2 this year, eight baseball teams banded together to form the National League. The teams were from Chicago, St. Louis, New York, Boston, Cincinnati, Louisville, Philadelphia, and Hartford.

- My hundreds, tens, and units digits are consecutive integers in reverse order; their mean is 7.
- My date is divisible by 2.
- The sum of all of my digits is 22.

What year am I?

February 3

On February 3 of this year, the 15th Amendment to the U.S. Constitution was ratified. This amendment granted citizens the right to vote, regardless of race, color, or previous condition of servitude.

- My date is divisible by 2, 5, and 10.
- My hundreds digit is equal to $\sqrt{64}$.
- The sum of all of my digits is 16.

What year am I?

On February 3 of this year, American illustrator Norman Rockwell was born. Many of his realistic illustrations appeared on the covers of the *Saturday Evening Post*.

- My hundreds and tens digits are consecutive integers whose sum is 17.
- My units digit is 50% of my hundreds digit.

What year am I?

February 4

On February 4 of this year, George Washington was named president of the United States by the Electoral College.

- My hundreds, tens, and units digits are consecutive integers whose mean is 8.
- The two-digit number formed by my tens and units digits is the second largest prime number < 100.

What year am I?

On February 4 of this year, the first Winter Olympics held in the United States began in Lake Placid, New York. Seventeen nations participated in the event. The U.S. bobsled team, led by William Fiske, won the gold medal with a time of 7:53.68.

- My date is divisible by 2, 3, and 6.
- The product of my tens and units digits is three less than my hundreds digit.
- The sum of all of my digits is 15.

What year am I?

February 5

On February 5 of this year, African-American baseball player Hank Aaron was born in Mobile, Alabama. Aaron topped Babe Ruth's batting average and became the all-time U.S. home run leader, with a career total of 755.

- My tens digit is $33\frac{1}{3}\%$ of my hundreds digit.
- The sum of my tens digit and units digit is 7.

What year am I?

On February 5 of this year, American statesman Adlai Stevenson was born in Los Angeles. Stevenson was governor of Illinois and a Democratic presidential candidate. He lost the 1952 presidential election to Dwight D. Eisenhower.

- The sum of my digits is only 10.
- My date written in scientific notation is 1.9×10^3.

What year am I?

February 6

On February 6 of this year, Babe Ruth was born in Baltimore, Maryland. A left-handed pitcher, he hit 714 home runs in 22 major league seasons and played in 10 World Series.

- My date is divisible by 5 but not 10.
- My hundreds and tens digits are consecutive integers; if they were the sides of a rectangle, its perimeter would be 34 and its area would be 72.

What year am I?

On February 6 of this year, Ronald Reagan was born in Tampico, Illinois. Before becoming the 40th president of the United States, he was a sportscaster, a movie actor, a rancher, and a businessman. He was the oldest man ever elected president.

- My hundreds digit and the two-digit number formed by my tens and units digits are consecutive odd integers whose sum is 20.
- Nonetheless, the sum of all of my digits is only 12.

What year am I?

February 7

On February 7 of this year, American author Sinclair Lewis was born in Sauk Centre, Minnesota. A Nobel Prize winner, Lewis wrote about the area he knew best: the American Midwest.

- My hundreds and tens digits are the same even number; if they were the sides of a square, its area would be 64.
- My units digit is the third prime number.

What year am I?

On February 7 of this year, Laura Ingalls Wilder was born. The author of the "Little House" series, she did not begin writing books until she was 65 years old.

- My hundreds, tens, and units digits are consecutive integers, but they are somewhat out of order.
- My tens digit is $\frac{3}{4}$ of my hundreds digit; my units digit is prime.
- The sum of all of my digits is 22.

What year am I?

February 8

On February 8 of this year, the Boy Scouts of America was incorporated in Washington, D.C., by William Boyce. It was modeled after the British Boy Scout Association.

- My date can be written as 1.91×10^3 in scientific notation.
- The sum of all of my digits is 11.

What year am I?

On February 8 of this year, French science fiction writer Jules Verne was born. He wrote many novels, including *Around the World in 80 Days* and *Twenty Thousand Leagues Under the Sea*.

- My hundreds and units digits are the same even number.
- My tens digit is the cube root of my hundreds digit.

What year am I?

February 9

On February 9 of this year, the U.S. Weather Bureau was established. Now known as the National Weather Service, most newspapers receive their weather information from this source.

- My date is divisible by 2, 5, and 10.
- The sum of my odd thousands and tens digits is equal to my hundreds digit.
- The sum of all of my digits is 16.

What year am I?

On February 9 of this year, an earthquake occurred in the San Fernando Valley in California. It registered 6.6 on the Richter scale and killed more than 60 people.

- If my tens digit were two greater, my number would be a palindrome.
- The sum of all of my digits is 18.

What year am I?

February 10

On February 10 of this year, the first "singing telegram" was delivered by Western Union.

- The product of my tens and units digits is equal to my hundreds digit.
- My tens and units digits could be the sides of a square with a perimeter of 12.
- The sum of all of my digits is 16.

What year am I?

On February 10 of this year, the familiar slogan "All the News That's Fit to Print" first appeared on the front page of the *New York Times*. The newspaper offered a prize of $100 to anyone who could come up with a better slogan of 10 words or less. Although thousands of submissions were received, none was judged to be better than the original. It is still the newspaper's slogan.

- My hundreds, tens, and units digits are consecutive integers that are all out of order.
- My hundreds digit is even; my tens and units digits are odd.
- Only my units digit is prime.
- The sum of all of my digits is 25.

What year am I?

February 11

On February 11 of this year, American inventor Thomas Alva Edison was born in Milan, Ohio. Edison held more than 1,200 patents, including the incandescent electric lamp, the phonograph, the electric dynamo, and key parts of today's movie camera. He said, "Genius is 1 percent inspiration and 99 percent perspiration."

- My tens digit is 50% of my hundreds digit.
- My units digit is one less than my hundreds digit.
- The sum of my digits is 20.

What year am I?

On February 11 of this year (B.C.), the Japanese nation was founded when Emperor Jimmu ascended to the throne. The national holiday is called National Foundation Day, and ceremonies are held with the emperor, empress, and many other dignitaries attending.

- My three-digit date is divisible by 2, 3, 5, 6, and 10.
- The two-digit number formed by my hundreds and tens digits is a multiple of 11.
- The sum of all of my digits is 12.

What year am I?

February 12

On February 12th of this year, Abraham Lincoln was born in Hardin County, Kentucky. The 16th president of the United States, he was in office during the Civil War and is known for his Emancipation Proclamation, the Gettysburg Address, and his proclamation making the fourth Thursday of November Thanksgiving Day. He was shot on Good Friday.

- My date is divisible by 3 and 9.
- The sum of my thousands and hundreds digits is equal to my units digit.
- The sum of all of my digits is 18.

What year am I?

On February 12 of this year, Alexander Graham Bell demonstrated the telephone with a line between Boston and Salem, Massachusetts.

- My tens and units digits are the same odd prime number.
- My hundreds digit minus one is equal to my tens digit.
- The sum of all of my digits is 23.

What year am I?

February 13

On February 13 of this year, American artist Grant Wood was born in Anamosa, Iowa. His most famous painting is called *American Gothic*. (Can you describe this painting?)

- My units digit is $\frac{1}{4}$ of my hundreds digit.
- The sum of my thousands and hundreds digits is equal to my tens digit.
- My hundreds and tens digits could be the sides of a rectangle with an area of 72 and a perimeter of 34.

What year am I?

On February 13 of this year, the first magazine was published in the United States. Called *American Magazine,* it was published by Andrew Bradford. It appeared three days before Benjamin Franklin's *General Magazine*.

- My hundreds, tens, and units digits form a palindrome with two prime numbers and one even number; its sum is 18.
- If my hundreds and units digits were the sides of a square, its perimeter would be 28.

What year am I?

February 14

On February 14 of this year, comedian Jack Benny (Benjamin Kubelsky) was born in Waukegan, Illinois. He had a radio show that lasted 20 years and also a very long-running television show.

- My units digit is 50% of my hundreds digit.
- The positive difference between my thousands and tens digits is equal to my hundreds digit.
- The sum of all of my digits is 22.

What year am I?

On February 14 of this year, Oregon became the 33rd state.

- The two-digit number formed by my tens and units digits is the largest prime in the 50's.
- The sum of my hundreds and thousands digits is equal to my units digit.

What year am I?

February 15

On February 15 of this year, the astronomer Galileo was born in Pisa, Italy. Galileo is credited with ushering in the "scientific method" and was ridiculed for exploring unpopular scientific theories. He once said, "We cannot discover new oceans unless we have the courage to lose sight of the shore."

- My hundreds digit is the third prime number.
- The two-digit number formed by my tens and units digits is equal to 2^6.
- The sum of all of my digits is 16.

What year am I?

On February 15 of this year, Susan B. Anthony was born. The leader of the women's suffrage movement, she was arrested and fined for voting—which at the time was illegal for women. She was the first woman to appear on an American coin.

- My date is divisible by 2, 5, and 10.
- If my tens and hundreds digits were the sides of a rectangle, its area would be 16 and its perimeter would be 20.

What year am I?

February 16

On February 16 of this year, the tomb of King Tutankhamen was opened by archaeologists. It had been sealed for more than 3,000 years.

- The two-digit number formed by my tens and units digits form the ninth prime number.
- My hundreds digit is 300% of my units digit.
- The sum of all of my digits is 15.

   What year am I?

On February 16 of this year, American ventriloquist Edgar Bergen was born in Chicago, Illinois. His dummies were called Charlie McCarthy, Mortimer Snerd, and Effie Klinker.

- My units digit is $33\frac{1}{3}$% of my hundreds digit.
- My tens digit is the additive identity.
- The sum of all of my digits is 13.

   What year am I?

February 17

On February 17 of this year, two thousand people attended a meeting in Washington, D.C., to organize the National Congress of Mothers—the forerunner of the Parent Teacher Association (PTA).

- The two-digit number formed by my tens and units digits is the largest prime number < 100.
- My hundreds digit is the largest single-digit Fibonnaci number.
- The sum of all of my digits is 25.

   What year am I?

On February 17 of this year, basketball and baseball player Michael Jordan was born in Wilmington, North Carolina.

- My units digit is $\frac{1}{2}$ of my tens digit but only $\frac{1}{3}$ of my hundreds digit.
- My tens digit is equal to 3!.
- The sum of all of my digits is 19.

   What year am I?

February 18

On February 18 of this year, Russian-born author and humorist Shalom Aleichem (the pen name for Solomon Rabinowitz) was born in the Ukraine. He was affectionately known in the United States as the "Jewish Mark Twain."

- The two-digit number formed by my tens and units digits is the largest prime number < 60.
- My hundreds digit is equal to 2^3.
- The sum of all of my digits is 23.

What year am I?

On February 18 of this year, American artist Louis Tiffany was born in New York City. The son of the famous jeweler, he is most remembered for his work with colored glass and Tiffany lamps.

- My tens digit is 50% of my hundreds digit.
- The two-digit number formed by my tens and units digits is a multiple of my hundreds digit.
- My hundreds and units digits could be the sides of a square with a perimeter of 32.

What year am I?

February 19

On February 19 of this year, Polish astronomer Nicolaus Copernicus was born. He revolutionized scientific thought, arguing that the sun was at the center of our planetary system and that the earth revolved around it. Many believe that this signaled the passage from medieval to modern thought.

- My hundreds digit is the only even square number less than 10.
- My tens and units digits form the 21st prime number.
- The sum of all of my digits is 15.

What year am I?

On February 19 of this year, Thomas Edison received a patent for the phonograph—the first "talking machine." Recordings at this time were made on wax cylinders.

- My hundreds, tens, and units digits form a palindrome with a sum of 23.
- My entire date is divisible by 2, 3, and 6.
- The sum of my digits is 24.

What year am I?

February 20

On February 20 of this year, basketball star Charles Barkley was born in Leeds, Alabama. Barkley is a starter for the Phoenix Suns.

- My tens digit is $\frac{2}{3}$ of my hundreds digit.
- My units digit is $\frac{1}{2}$ of my tens digit.
- The sum of all of my digits is 19.

What year am I?

On February 20 of this year, astronaut John Glenn became the first American to orbit the earth. He circled the globe three times before landing.

- My date is divisible by 2, 3, 6, and 9.
- My tens digit is $\frac{2}{3}$ of my hundreds digit.
- My units digit is $\frac{1}{3}$ of my tens digit.
- The sum of all of my digits is 18.

What year am I?

February 21

On February 21 of this year, Lucy B. Hobbs became the first woman to graduate from a dental school in the United States.

- My date is divisible by 2, 3, and 6.
- If you square my hundreds digit and add 2, you will get the two-digit number formed by my tens and units digits.
- My tens and units digits could be the sides of a square with a perimeter of 24.
- The sum of all of my digits is 21.

What year am I?

On February 21 of this year, black militant Malcolm X was shot and killed in New York City. He was born Malcolm Little, the son of a Baptist preacher, in Omaha, Nebraska.

- My tens and units digits are consecutive integers (in reverse order) whose sum is 11 and whose product is 30.
- My date is divisible by 3 and 5 but not by 10.
- The sum of all of my digits is 21.

What year am I?

February 22

On February 22 of this year, Augustine and Mary Washington became the proud parents of GeorgeWashington in Westmoreland County, Virginia.

- My tens and units digits are consecutive integers (in reverse order) whose sum is 5 and whose product is 6.
- My date is divisible by 2.
- The sum of all of my digits is 13.

What year am I?

On February 22 of this year, the leaders of the Montgomery bus boycott were arrested when they refused to end the three-month-old constraint. Among those arrested, finger-printed, and jailed were Rosa Parks and Dr. Martin Luther King, Jr. The story of their arrest was carried in newspapers all over the world.

- My tens and units digits are consecutive integers whose sum is 11 and product is 30.
- My hundreds digit is 150% of my units digit.
- My date is divisible by 2, 3, and 6.

What year am I?

February 23

On February 23 of this year, members of the 5th U.S. Marine division planted an American flag atop Mount Suribachi on Iwo Jima. This act was memorialized in a very famous photograph.

- The sum of my consecutive tens and units digits is equal to my hundreds digit.
- My date is divisible by 5 but not 10.
- The sum of all of my digits is 19.

What year am I?

On February 23 of this year, the siege of the Alamo began in San Antonio, Texas.

- The two-digit number formed by my tens and units digits is equal to 6^2.
- The sum of my thousands and hundreds digits is equal to the sum of my tens and units digits.
- The sum of all of my digits is 18.

What year am I?

February 24

On February 24 of this year, Wilhelm Karl Grimm was born. He was one of the German "Brothers Grimm" who compiled *Grimm's Fairy Tales*.

- My hundreds and tens digits are consecutive integers whose product is 56.
- My date is divisible by 2.
- My units digit is two less than my tens digit; both are even numbers.

What year am I?

On February 24 of this year, Mexico declared its independence from Spain.

- My thousands and units digits are the same.
- My tens digit is 25% of my hundreds digit.
- The sum of all of my digits is 12.

What year am I?

February 25

On February 25 of this year, French Impressionist painter Pierre-Auguste Renoir was born in Limoges, France. Renoir is noted for his delicate use of color and light.

- My tens digit is 50% of my hundreds digit.
- My thousands and units digits are the multiplicative identity.
- The sum of all of my digits is 14.

What year am I?

On February 25 of this year, Hiram R. Revels became the first black man to be elected to the U.S. Senate from Mississippi. While in the Senate, he voted to end segregation in workplaces, schools, and railroads. Revels sponsored Michael Howard, the first black American to go to West Point.

- The sum of my thousands and tens digits is equal to my hundreds digit.
- My date is divisible by 2, 5, and 10.
- The sum of all of my digits is 16.

What year am I?

February 26

On February 26 of this year, Jackie Gleason was born in Brooklyn, New York. The musician, comedian, and actor was best known for his role as Ralph Kramden in the television series *The Honeymooners*.

- The two-digit number formed by my tens and units digits is equal to 2^4.
- The sum of all of my digits is 17.

What year am I?

On February 26 of this year, William Frederick Cody (Buffalo Bill) was born in Scott County, Iowa. He was the subject of many Wild West stories and became a very successful showman, taking his act across the United States and to Europe.

- My hundreds, tens, and units digits are all different even numbers.
- My tens digit is $\frac{1}{2}$ of my hundreds digit; my units digit is $1\frac{1}{2}$ times my tens digit.
- The sum of all of my digits is 19.

What year am I?

February 27

On February 27 of this year, author John Steinbeck was born in Salinas, California. Steinbeck wrote about his own area and the plight of migrant workers.

- My date is divisible by 2, 3, and 6.
- My units digit is one greater than my thousands digit.
- The sum of my thousands and units digits is $\frac{1}{3}$ of my hundreds digit.
- The sum of all of my digits is 12.

What year am I?

On February 27 of this year, poet Henry Wadsworth Longfellow was born in Portland, Maine. You might enjoy his poems "The Midnight Ride of Paul Revere," "The Song of Hiawatha," and "The Wreck of the Hesperus."

- My units digit is the largest single-digit prime number.
- My hundreds digit is one more than my units digit.
- The sum of all of my digits is 16.

What year am I?

February 28

On February 28 of this year, the final episode of the TV show *M*A*S*H* aired. This was the last of the show's 255 episodes and was watched by over 75% of the viewing public.

- The two-digit number formed by my tens and units digits is the third largest prime number < 100.
- My units digit is $\frac{1}{3}$ of my hundreds digit.
- The sum of all of my digits is 21.

What year am I?

On February 28 of this year, the Territory of Colorado was organized.

- My tens digit is $\frac{3}{4}$ of my hundreds digit.
- My thousands and units digits are the multiplicative identity.
- The sum of all of my digits is 16.

What year am I?

February 29

On February 29 of this year, poet Howard Nemerov was born in New York City. The third poet laureate of the United States, he won a Pulitzer Prize. As poet laureate, he wrote a verse to commemorate the launch of the space shuttle *Atlantis*.

- My date is divisible by 2, 3, 5, 6, and 10.
- My hundreds digit is three times the sum of my thousands and tens digits.

What year am I?

On February 29 of this year, astronaut Jack Lousma was born in Grand Rapids, Michigan.

- My tens digit is $\frac{1}{3}$ of my hundreds digit but $\frac{1}{2}$ of my units digit.
- The two-digit number formed by my tens and units digits is a multiple of my hundreds digit.
- The sum of all of my digits is 19.

What year am I?

March 1

On March 1 of this year, Yellowstone National Park was created by Congress. The geyser "Old Faithful" is located in this park.

- My date is divisible by 2.
- My units digit is $\frac{1}{4}$ of my hundreds digit.
- My tens digit is the largest single-digit prime.

What year am I?

On March 1 of this year, the Peace Corps was established by President John F. Kennedy's executive order. Since this year, more than 150,000 volunteers have traveled to 94 countries to teach people how to help themselves. The volunteers help people in the areas of health, education, water sanitation, agriculture, nutrition, and forestry.

- If my hundreds digit were three less, my date would be a palindrome.
- The sum of all of my digits is 17.

What year am I?

March 2

On March 2 of this year, author and illustrator Dr. Seuss (Theodor Seuss Geisel) was born in Springfield, Massachusetts. (Can you think of some of his popular books?)

- Both my hundreds and units digits are square numbers, but my hundreds is odd and my units is even.
- My tens digit is one less than my thousands digit.

What year am I?

On March 2 of this year, the first school for the blind in America was established in Massachusetts.

- The two-digit number formed by my tens and units digits is the 10th prime number.
- The sum of all of my digits is 20.

What year am I?

March 3

On March 3 of this year, "The Star-Spangled Banner" officially became the national anthem of the United States.

- My tens digit is $\frac{1}{3}$ of my hundreds digit.
- My thousands and units digits are both the multiplicative identity.

What year am I?

On March 3 of this year, heptathlon athlete Jackie (Jacqueline) Joyner-Kersee was born in East St. Louis, Illinois. She is an Olympic gold medal winner in the heptathlon and long jump and holds the world record for points set in the heptathlon (7,291 points). (What does the prefix *hept* stand for in her Olympic event?)

- My tens digit is $\frac{2}{3}$ of my hundreds digit.
- My units digit is $\frac{2}{3}$ of my tens digit.
- The sum of my digits is 18.

What year am I?

March 4

On March 4 of this year, the U.S. Constitution became effective. The first Congress met in New York under the rules of the new "law of the land."

- My hundreds, ten, and units digits are consecutive integers whose mean is 8.
- The sum of my digits is 25.

What year am I?

On March 4 of this year, Vermont was admitted as the 14th state.

- My hundreds and tens digits are consecutive odd integers whose product is 63.
- My thousands and units digits could be the beginning and end of a palindrome.

What year am I?

March 5

On March 5 of this year, American painter and lithographer James Merritt Ives was born. Ives and Nathaniel Currier depicted America during its westward expansion; they were among the first pictorial reporters. Currier and Ives prints are still used as symbols of the "American scene."

- My hundreds, tens, and units digits are all even numbers.
- My units digit is $\frac{1}{2}$ of my hundreds digit; my tens digit is $\frac{1}{2}$ of my units digit.

What year am I?

On March 5 of this year, actor Rex Harrison was born in Huyton, England. He starred in many movies; one of his most popular roles was the role of the doctor in *Doctor Doolittle*.

- The sum of my thousands and units digits is equal to my hundreds digit.
- My date is divisible by 2, 3, 4, and 6.
- The sum of my digits is 18.

What year am I?

March 6

On March 6 of this year, painter and sculptor Michelangelo (Buonarroti) was born in the Italian town of Caprese, Tuscany.

- The sum of my thousands and hundreds digits is equal to my units digit.
- My date is divisible by 5 but not 2.
- The sum of all of my digits is 17.

What year am I?

On March 6 of this year, the first automobile was driven by Charles Brady King in Detroit.

- My units digit is 75% of my hundreds digit.
- My units digit is $\frac{2}{3}$ of my tens digit.
- My date is divisible by 2, 3, 4, and 6.
- The sum of all of my digits is 24.

What year am I?

March 7

On March 7 of this year, Alexander Graham Bell patented the telephone.

- My units digit is $\frac{3}{4}$ of my hundreds digit.
- My date is even.
- The sum of my thousands and tens digits is equal to my hundreds digit.

   What year am I?

On March 7 of this year, American naturalist and author Luther Burbank was born in Lancaster, Massachusetts. He is the creator and developer of many new varieties of flowers, fruits, vegetables, and trees. His birthday is observed by some as Bird and Arbor Day.

- The two-digit number formed by my tens and units digits is equal to 7^2.
- The sum of my digits is 22.

   What year am I?

March 8

On March 8 of this year, former U.S. Supreme Court Justice Oliver Wendell Holmes was born. Holmes said, "Bigotry is like the pupil of the eye; the more light you pour on it, the more it will contract," and "Taxes are what we pay for civilized society."

- My tens digit is 50% of my hundreds digit.
- My units digit is the multiplicative identity.
- The sum of all of my digits is 14.

   What year am I?

On March 8 of this year, this day was proclaimed as International Women's Day. This day to honor women—especially working women—was proclaimed at a conference of women held in Helsinki, Finland. It is unusual among holidays in that it is celebrated all over the world, even in the People's Republic of China.

- My date is divisible by 5 and 10.
- My thousands, hundreds, and tens digits form a palindrome whose sum is 11.

   What year am I?

March 9

On March 9 of this year, Italian navigator and explorer Amerigo Vespucci was born in Florence, Italy. He sailed to the coast of South America, where he discovered the Amazon and Plate rivers. While his exploits did not achieve the fame of Columbus, the New World was named for Amerigo Vespucci by a German geographer and mapmaker named Martin Waldseemüller.

- My hundreds and tens digits are consecutive integers whose product is 20.
- If my tens digit were reduced by one, my hundreds, tens, and units digits would be the same.

What year am I?

On March 9 of this year, American inventor Howard Hathaway Aiken was born. Aiken invented the first modern digital computer, which weighed 35 tons, was 51 feet long, and could only do arithmetic.

- My date is divisible by many numbers including 2, 4, 5, and 10.
- My tens and units digits are the same.
- My date is written 1.9×10^3 in scientific notation.

What year am I?

March 10

On March 10 of this year, American abolitionist Harriet Tubman died in Auburn, New York. Ms. Tubman escaped from a Maryland plantation and formed the "Underground Railroad." Through her efforts, more than 300 slaves reached freedom.

- The two-digit numbers formed by my thousands and hundreds digits and my tens and units digits are both prime numbers.
- One is the sixth prime number and the other is the eighth prime number.

What year am I?

On March 10 of this year, the Salvation Army was established in the United States by Commissioner George Scott Railton and seven women officers.

- If my units digit were one greater, my date would be a palindrome with a sum of 18.
- My date is divisible by 2, 5, and 10.

What year am I?

March 11

On March 11 of this year, clergyman and American civil rights leader Ralph David Abernathy was born in Linden, Alabama.

- My date is divisible by 2, 3, 6, and 9.
- My units digit is $66\frac{2}{3}\%$ of my hundreds digit.
- My tens digit is $33\frac{1}{3}\%$ of my units digit.

   What year am I?

March 11 of this year is believed to be the anniversary of the death of Johnny Appleseed (John Chapman). He planted orchards of apples and was considered a great medicine man by the Indians.

- The sum of my tens and units digits is equal to 3^2.
- My tens digit is 50% of my hundreds digit.
- The sum of all of my digits is 18.

   What year am I?

March 12

On March 12 of this year, the most devastating blizzard of recent times hit the Northeast. A snowfall of 40 to 50 inches, accompanied by gale force winds, left drifts as high as 30 to 40 feet. More than 400 persons died in the storm—200 in New York City alone.

- My hundreds, tens, and units digits could be the sides of a cube with a volume of 512 cubic units.

   What year am I?

On March 12 of this year, the first parachute jump from an airplane in the United States was made. (What do you think the statement "Minds are like parachutes; they only function when they are open" means?)

- The two-digit number formed by my tens and units digits could be the perimeter of a rectangle with a length of 4 and a width of 2.
- The sum of my digits is 13.

   What year am I?

March 13

On March 13 of this year, Percival Lowell was born in Boston, Massachusetts. The founder of the Lowell Observatory in Flagstaff, Arizona, Lowell began the search for the planet Pluto. It took 25 years to find the planet.

- My tens and units digits could be the sides of a square with a perimeter of 20 and an area of 25.
- The sum of all of my digits is 19.

What year am I?

On March 13 of this year, German-born English astronomer Sir William Herschel discovered Uranus, the planet seventh farthest from the sun.

- If my tens and units digits were reversed, they would form a two-digit number that is one greater than the two-digit number formed by my thousands and hundreds digits.
- My hundreds and tens digits are consecutive integers with a product of 56.
- The two-digit number formed by my thousands and hundreds digits is a prime number.

What year am I?

March 14

On March 14 of this year, Albert Einstein was born in Ulm, Germany. The theoretical physicist is best known for his theory of relativity. He immigrated to the United States and won a Nobel Prize for his work.

- My tens and units digits are consecutive odd integers whose sum is 16.
- The sum of my thousands and hundreds digits is equal to my units digit.

What year am I?

On March 14 of this year, Casey Jones (John Luther Jones) was born near Cayce, Kentucky. He was a railroad engineer and the hero of the song "The Ballad of Casey Jones." He died bravely in a railroad wreck when he was only 36.

- My hundreds, tens, and units digits are consecutive even integers in reverse order; their mean is 6.
- My tens digit is $\frac{3}{4}$ of my hundreds digit; my units digit is $\frac{2}{3}$ of my tens digit.

What year am I?

March 15

On March 15 of this year, Andrew Jackson was born in a log cabin in Waxhaw, South Carolina. Nicknamed "Old Hickory," the seventh president of the United States had a reputation as a brawler and reportedly participated in countless duels. He was one of our most offbeat presidents.

- My hundreds, tens, and units digits form a palindrome with a sum of 20.
- My hundreds and units digits are the largest single-digit prime number.

What year am I?

On March 15 of this year (B.C.), Julius Caesar was assassinated. The day is called the Ides of March.

- My tens and units digits are very lonely digits because they're all alone.
- My tens and units digits could be the sides of a square with an area of 16.
- The sum of my digits is 8.

What year am I?

March 16

On March 16 of this year, James Madison was born in Port Conway, Virginia. The fourth president of the United States, he was in office when the British invaded Washington, D.C. He escaped with other officials while the capital burned.

- The two-digit number formed by my tens and units digits is a multiple of 17.
- If my tens digit were two greater, my date would be a palindrome.

What year am I?

On March 16 of this year, the first black newspaper in the United States was published in New York City. It was called *Freedom's Journal*. The day is now celebrated as Black Press Day in New York.

- The two-digit number formed by my tens and units digits is a multiple of the sum of my thousands and hundreds digits.
- My tens digit is the cube root of my hundreds digit.

What year am I?

March 17

On March 17 of this year, Nat "King" Cole was born in Montgomery, Alabama. He started playing the piano at the age of 4 and was the first black entertainer to host a national TV show. His many songs include "The Christmas Song," "Mona Lisa," and "Unforgettable."

- The two-digit number formed by my thousands and hundreds digits is the same as the two-digit number formed by my tens and units digits.
- My tens and units digits could be the sides of a rectangle with a perimeter of 20 and an area of 9.

What year am I?

On March 17 of this year, ballet star Rudolf Nureyev was born on a train in Siberia. He defected from the Soviet Union while on a ballet tour. Nureyev was the artistic director of the Paris Ballet.

- My hundreds digit is three times the size of my tens digit.
- The two-digit number formed by my tens and units digits is a multiple of 19.
- My date is divisible by 2, 3, and 6.

What year am I?

March 18

On March 18 of this year, Grover Cleveland was born in Caldwell, New Jersey. The 22nd and 24th president of the United States, he was the only president to serve two nonconsecutive terms. He ran for the intervening term and won the popular vote but lost the Electoral College vote. He was the first president to be married and father a child in the White House.

- The two-digit number formed by my tens and units digits is the 12th prime number.
- My hundreds digit is equal to 2^3.

What year am I?

On March 18 of this year, the first electric razor was marketed by Schick, Inc.

- My hundreds digit is 300% of my tens digit.
- The two-digit number formed by my tens and units digits is the 11th prime number.

What year am I?

March 19

On March 19 of this year, the swallows first returned to the old mission at San Juan Capistrano, California.

- If my units digits were reduced by five, my date would be a palindrome.
- My date is divisible by 2, 3, and 6.
- The sum of all of my digits is 21.

What year am I?

On March 19 of this year, U.S. Congresswoman Edith Nourse Rogers was born in Saco, Maine. Elected to fill the seat of her deceased husband, she served 17 elected terms, was the first woman to have her name attached to important legislation, and was responsible for the legislation that created the Women's Army Auxiliary Corps during World War II.

- My date is a palindrome with a sum of 18.

What year am I?

March 20

On March 20 of this year, Harriet Beecher Stowe's novel *Uncle Tom's Cabin* was published. The book had a tremendous impact on public feeling in the United States in the years leading up to the Civil War.

- My units digit is $\frac{1}{4}$ of my hundreds digit.
- The prime factorization of the two-digit number formed by my tens and units digits is $2^2 \times 13$.

What year am I?

On March 20 of this year, children rang the United Nations peace bell in New York City for the first celebration of Earth Day. The bell sounded at the exact moment when the sun crossed the equator, the beginning of spring in the northern hemisphere.

- My tens and units digits could be the sides of a rectangle with a perimeter of 32 and an area of 63.
- My hundreds, tens, and units digits form a palindrome with a sum of 25.

What year am I?

March 21

On March 21 of this year, Mexican resistance hero Benito Pablo Juárez was born to Zapotec Indian parents. Orphaned at an early age, he became the symbol of Mexican resistance to foreign intervention.

- My units digit is equal to 3!.
- My hundreds digit is two more than my units digit.
- My tens digit is the additive identity.

What year am I?

On March 21 of this year, Pocahontas died in England. The daughter of a Native American woman, she was responsible for fostering goodwill between the new American colonists and her people. She married English settler John Rolfe. During a trip to England, she helped raise money to support the colony of Jamestown. She died before returning home.

- The two-digit number formed by my thousands and hundreds digits and the two-digit number formed by my tens and units digits are consecutive integers with a sum of 33.
- My hundreds digit is perfect; my units digit is prime.
- The sum of all of my digits is 15.

What year am I?

March 22

On March 22 of this year, the first women's collegiate basketball game was played at Smith College in Northampton, Massachusetts. Sandra Berenson, the "Mother of Women's Basketball," supervised the game.

- My hundreds and tens digits are consecutive integers with a sum of 17 and a product of 72.
- My units digit is $\frac{1}{3}$ of my tens digit.
- The sum of all of my digits is 21.

What year am I?

On March 22 of this year, William Shatner (Captain Kirk of the starship *Enterprise*) was born in Montreal, Quebec, Canada.

- The two-digit number formed by my tens and units digits is a prime number that is 12 greater than the prime number formed by my thousands and hundreds digits.
- The sum of all of my digits is 14.

What year am I?

March 23

On March 23 of this year, Patrick Henry delivered his "Give me liberty or give me death" speech.

- My date is divisible by 5 but not by 10.
- My hundreds and tens digits could be the sides of a square with an area of 49.

What year am I?

On March 23 of this year, mathematician Emmy Noether was born in Erlangen, Germany. She received a doctoral degree in mathematics from the University of Erlangen. She was forced to leave Germany when the Nazis came into power (she was Jewish); she came to the United States and taught at Bryn Mawr College.

- My hundreds and tens digits could be the sides of a square with a perimeter of 32.
- My units digit is 25% of my tens digit.

What year am I?

March 24

On March 24 of this year, magician and escape artist Harry Houdini was born in Budapest, Hungary. He was best known for his ability to escape from handcuffs, straitjackets, and locked boxes.

- My units digit is 50% of my hundreds digit.
- The two-digit number formed by my tens and units digits is a multiple of 37.
- The prime factors of the two-digit number formed by my thousands and hundreds digits is 2×3^2.

What year am I?

On March 24 of this year, Dorothy Stratton was born in Brookfield, Missouri. She was the organizer of SPARS (the women's branch of the Coast Guard). Under her command, 10,000 women were trained for supportive noncombat roles during World War II.

- My hundreds, tens, and units digits form a palindrome with a sum of 25.
- My hundreds and units digits are cubic numbers; my tens digit is square.

What year am I?

March 25

On March 25 of this year, American sculptor Gutzon Borglum was born in Bear Lake, Idaho. At Mount Rushmore Memorial Park, he created the sculptures of Washington, Jefferson, Lincoln, and Theodore Roosevelt, working on them for 14 years.

- My tens digit is 75% of my hundreds digit.
- My tens and units digits are consecutive integers; if they were the sides of a rectangle, its area would be 42.

What year am I?

On March 25 of this year, the Triangle Shirtwaist Fire broke out at about 4:30 P.M. in New York City. Although the fire lasted only 18 minutes, it left 146 workers dead—most of them poor immigrant women. The tragic fire became a turning point in labor history, bringing about reforms in health and safety laws.

- If my tens digit were eight greater, my date would be a palindrome.
- The sum of my digits is 12.

What year am I?

March 26

On March 26 of this year, Jonas Salk introduced the polio vaccine in the United States.

- My tens and units digits are consecutive primes in reverse order; their product is 15.
- My hundreds digit is 300% of my units digit.

What year am I?

On March 26 of this year, actor Leonard Nimoy was born in Boston, Massachusetts. He played Spock in *Star Trek*.

- If my tens digit were three times its size, my date would be a palindrome.
- The sum of all of my digits is 14.

What year am I?

March 27

On March 27 of this year, jazz singer Sarah Vaughan was born in Newark, New Jersey. She began her career at 19 when she won a contest at New York's Apollo Theater. Her voice was so magnificent she was nicknamed "Divine One."

- The two-digit number formed by my tens and units digits is equal to 4! .
- My hundreds digit is one more than the product of my tens and units digits.

What year am I?

On March 27 of this year, German scientist Wilhelm Roentgen was born in Munich, Germany. A Nobel Prize winner, he discovered X rays.

- My date is a multiple of 5.
- My units and tens digits are consecutive integers with a sum of 9 and a product of 20.
- The sum of all of my digits is 18.

What year am I?

March 28

On March 28 of this year, accidents at the Three Mile Island nuclear plant near Harrisburg, Pennsylvania, almost brought about a meltdown of the uranium core. The accidents led to an examination of the safety of nuclear plants all over the United States.

- The two-digit number formed by my tens and units digits is the largest prime < 80.
- My hundreds, tens, and units digits form a palindrome with a sum of 25.

What year am I?

On March 28 of this year, Italian Renaissance painter Raphael was born. Two of his well-known paintings are *The Three Graces* and the Sistine *Madonna*.

- My hundreds digit is 50% of my tens digit.
- The sum of my thousands and units digits is equal to my hundreds digit.
- The prime factors of the two-digit number formed by my hundreds and tens digits is $2^4 \times 3$.

What year am I?

March 29

On March 29 of this year, John Tyler was born in Charles City County, Virginia. The 10th president of the United States, Tyler succeeded to the presidency upon the death of William Henry Harrison.

- My date is divisible by 2, 5, and 10.
- My hundreds and tens digits are consecutive odd integers whose product is 63 and sum is 16.

What year am I?

On March 29 of this year, actress and singer Pearl Bailey was born in Newport News, Virginia.

- The two-digit number formed by my tens and units digits is one less than the two-digit number formed by my thousands and hundreds digits.
- The sum of all of my digits is 19.

What year am I?

March 30

On March 30 of this year, Dutch Postimpressionist painter Vincent van Gogh was born in Groot Zundert, Holland.

- The two-digit number formed by my tens and units digits is the 16th prime number.
- The sum of all of my digits is 17.

What year am I?

On March 30 of this year, Spanish painter Francisco José de Goya was born in Aragon, Spain. It is estimated that he produced more than 1,800 paintings, drawings, and etchings during his lifetime.

- My date is divisible by 2, 3, 6, and 9.
- My tens and units digits are consecutive even numbers with a sum of 10.

What year am I?

March 31

On March 31 of this year, chemist Robert Wilhelm Eberhard von Bunsen was born in Göttingen, Germany. His invention of the Bunsen burner provided chemists with an indispensable instrument—a burner that allows the user to regulate the proportions of flammable gas and air to create the most efficient flame.

- My tens and units digits form the smallest two-digit prime number.
- The sum of all of my digits is 11.

What year am I?

On March 31 of this year, Franz Joseph Haydn was born in Rohrau, Austria-Hungary. The "Father of the Symphony," he composed 120 symphonies, more than 100 works for chamber groups, a dozen operas, and hundreds of other musical works. He died at the age of 67.

- My hundreds, tens, and units digits are all prime, but only my units digit is even.
- My tens digit is four less than my hundreds digit.
- The sum of all of my digits is 13.

What year am I?

April 1

On April 1 of this year, mathematician Sophie Germain was born in Paris, France. Her parents did not approve of her studies and felt that girls should not be straining their minds on "such nonsense as mathematics." Sophie would light candles after her parents were asleep and study all night. As she grew up, she wrote papers under the pen name M. Le Blanc so people would think she was a man and the papers would be published.

- My hundreds and tens digits could be the sides of a square with an area of 49.
- My units digit is a perfect number.

What year am I?

On April 1 of this year, Indian political leader Jagjivan Ram was born. He was born into a family of "untouchables" and was the first of that caste to attend university. He was a champion and spokesperson for India's 100 million untouchables; he overcame most of the handicaps of the caste system.

- My hundreds digit is an odd square number; my units digit is an even cubic number.
- The sum of all of my digits is 18.

What year am I?

April 2

On April 2 of this year, Hans Christian Andersen was born in Odense, Denmark. Andersen wrote more than 150 fairy tales, regarded as classics in children's literature.

- My date is divisible by 5 but not 10.
- My hundreds digit is three greater than my units digit.
- The sum of my digits is 14.

What year am I?

On April 2 of this year, French sculptor Frédéric-Auguste Bartholdi was born. He created *Liberty Enlightening the World*, which stands in New York Harbor. (What is the more common name of this piece of sculpture?)

- My date is divisible by 2.
- My tens and units digits are consecutive integers whose sum is 7.
- My hundreds digit is 200% of my units digit.

What year am I?

April 3

On April 3 of this year, American author Washington Irving was born in New York City. He wrote "Rip Van Winkle" and "The Legend of Sleepy Hollow."

- Both my hundreds and units digits are prime numbers.
- My hundreds and tens digits could be the sides of a rectangle with an area of 56 and a perimeter of 30.
- One more than twice my units digit is equal to my hundreds digit.

What year am I?

On April 3 of this year, American author and clergyman Edward Everett Hale was born. He wrote the short story "A Man Without a Country."

- My tens and units digits are the same number; they are equal to $\sqrt[3]{8}$.
- My hundreds digit is equal to 2^3.

What year am I?

April 4

On April 4 of this year, American social reformer Dorothea Lynde Dix was born in Hampden, Maine. She left home at the age of 10 and was teaching by the time she was 14. She founded a home for girls in Boston in her teens. She was a vigorous fighter for humane conditions in insane asylums, jails, and other state-supported institutions.

- My date is divisible by 2.
- My units digit is 25% of my hundreds digit.
- My tens digit is two less than my units digit.

What year am I?

On April 4 of this year, the Reverend Martin Luther King, Jr., was assassinated in Memphis, Tennessee. James Earl Ray is serving a 99-year sentence for the crime.

- My date is divisible by 2, 3, and 6.
- My tens and units digits are consecutive even integers; if they were the sides of a rectangle, it would have an area of 48.
- The sum of my digits is 24.

What year am I?

April 5

On April 5 of this year, black educator and leader Booker T. Washington was born in Franklin County, Virginia. He wrote, "No race can prosper till it learns that there is as much dignity in tilling a field as in writing a poem."

- My tens and units digits are consecutive integers; if they were the lengths of the sides of a rectangle, it would have a perimeter of 22.
- The sum of my digits is 20.

What year am I?

On April 5 of this year, Colin Luther Powell was born in New York City. At one point he served as Chairman of the U.S. Joint Chiefs of Staff.

- My tens digit is $33\frac{1}{3}$% of my hundreds digit; both are odd numbers.
- My units digit is the largest single-digit prime number.
- The sum of my digits is 20.

What year am I?

April 6

On April 6 of this year, Robert E. Peary and Matthew Henson reached the North Pole.

- My hundreds, tens, and units digits form a palindrome.
- My hundreds and units digits are both square numbers.
- The sum of this palindrome makes it divisible by 3 and 9.

What year am I?

On April 6 of this year, the United States entered into World War I against Germany.

- The two-digit number formed by my tens and units digits is the seventh prime number.
- My date is divisible by 3 and 9.
- The sum of all of my digits is 18.

What year am I?

April 7

On April 7 of this year, American botanist and explorer David Fairchild was born in East Lansing, Michigan. Fairchild was noted for his studies of tropical plant species such as avocados and mangoes.

- My tens digit is $\frac{3}{4}$ of my hundreds digit.
- My tens digit is $\frac{2}{3}$ of my units digit.

What year am I?

On April 7 of this year, Asian-Indian musician Ravi Shankar was born. Much of his music was written for an Indian musical instrument called the sitar.

- My date is divisible by 2, 5, and 10.
- The square root of my hundreds digit minus my thousands digit equals my tens digit.
- The sum of all of my digits is 12.

What year am I?

April 8

On April 8 of this year, American neurosurgeon and Pulitzer Prize author Harvey Cushing was born. Cushing's medical advances were possible partly because anesthesia had already been developed; this is an example of how one accomplishment is dependent on those that have come before. Cushing also developed an instrument that measured blood pressure.

- My hundreds digit is equal to 2^3; my units digit is equal to 3^2.
- My tens digit is a perfect number.

What year am I?

On April 8 of this year, Henry "Hank" Aaron hit the 715th home run of his career and broke the record set by Babe Ruth. He finished his career with a total of 755 home runs.

- The prime factorization of the two-digit number formed by my tens and units digits is 2×37.
- The sum of all of my digits is 21.

What year am I?

April 9

On April 9 of this year, General Robert E. Lee, commander of the Army of Northern Virginia, surrendered to General Ulysses S. Grant, commander-in-chief of the Union Army, ending four years of civil war. The number of people who died during the Civil War is estimated at more than 500,000.

- My tens digit is 75% of my hundreds digit.
- My date is odd and divisible by 5.

What year am I?

On April 9 of this year, African-American opera singer Marian Anderson sang in an open-air Easter concert from the steps of the Lincoln Memorial in Washington, D.C., to an audience of over 75,000 people. She had been denied use of the Daughters of the American Revolution (D.A.R.) Constitution Hall, and so her concert became a protest against discrimination. Eleanor Roosevelt, the wife of the president, resigned from the D.A.R. in protest.

- My tens digit is the square root of my hundreds digit; my units digit is equal to my tens digit squared.
- The sum of all of my digits is 22.

What year am I?

April 10

On April 10 of this year, Frances Perkins was born in Boston, Massachusetts. The first woman member of a U.S. presidential cabinet, she was appointed Secretary of Labor by Franklin Delano Roosevelt.

- My units digit is the first prime number.
- My hundreds and tens digits are the same.
- The sum of my digits is 19.

What year am I?

On April 10 of this year, Jackie Robinson was recruited by the Brooklyn Dodgers. He was the first black in a major league baseball club.

- The sum of my even tens digit and my prime units digit is one greater than the sum of my odd thousands and hundreds digits.
- The sum of my digits is 21, making my date divisible by 3.

What year am I?

April 11

On April 11 of this year, the American Society for the Prevention of Cruelty to Animals was chartered in New York State.

- The sum of my digits is 21, and my date is divisible by 2, 3, and 6.
- My tens and units digits are the same number; each one is $\frac{3}{4}$ of my hundreds digit.

What year am I?

On April 11 of this year, Charles Evans Hughes was born in Glens Falls, New York. He was the 11th chief justice of the U.S. Supreme Court.

- My tens digit is 75% of my hundreds digit.
- My units digit is 25% of my hundreds digit.
- The sum of my digits is 17.

What year am I?

April 12

On April 12 of this year, the wind reached the highest velocity ever recorded. At the Mount Washington Observatory in New Hampshire, weather observers Wendell Stevenson, Alexander McKenzie, and Salvatore Pagliuca observed and recorded gusts reaching more than 231 miles per hour—"the strongest natural wind ever recorded on the earth's surface."

- My tens and units digits are consecutive integers whose sum is 7.
- My date is divisible by 2.
- My hundreds digit is 300% of my tens digit.

What year am I?

On April 12 of this year, comedian and TV personality David Letterman was born in Indianapolis, Indiana.

- The two-digit number formed by my tens and units digits is the 15th prime number.
- Both my hundreds and tens digits are square but one is odd and the other is even.

What year am I?

April 13

On April 13 of this year, Thomas Jefferson was born in Albermarle County, Virginia. Jefferson, the third president of the United States, was principal author of the Declaration of Independence. In addition to political philosophy, he studied architecture, science, and education. He wrote his own epitaph: "Here is buried Thomas Jefferson, author of the Declaration of American Independence, of the statute of Virginia for religious freedom, and father of the University of Virginia."

- My tens and units digits are consecutive integers whose product is 12, but my date is not even.
- My hundreds digit is a prime number.
- The sum of all of my digits is 15.

What year am I?

On April 13 of this year, New York's Metropolitan Museum of Art was opened to the public. It is the largest art museum in the United States.

- My date is divisible by 2, 5, and 10.
- My prime tens digit is one less than my hundreds digit.

What year am I?

April 14

On April 14 of this year, Abraham Lincoln was shot while watching a performance of *Our American Cousin* at Ford's Theater in Washington, D.C. He died the following day. The assassin was a young actor, John Wilkes Booth.

- My hundreds and tens digits are consecutive even numbers in reverse order.
- My date is divisible by 5.
- The sum of all of my digits is 20.

What year am I?

On April 14 of this year, Anne Sullivan was born. She was the teacher and companion of Helen Keller, the remarkable girl who was both blind and deaf.

- My tens and units digits could be the sides of a square with a perimeter of 24.
- My hundreds digit is a cubic number.

What year am I?

April 15

On April 15 of this year, mathematician Leonhard Euler was born. He was the first to use the symbol pi (π), and he published a list of 30 pairs of amicable numbers. (Can you find out what makes a number *amicable*?)

- My hundreds, tens, and units digits form a palindrome with a sum of 14.
- My tens digit is the additive identity.
- My hundreds digit is the largest single-digit prime.

What year am I?

On April 15 of this year, Italian Renaissance artist and scientist Leonardo da Vinci was born. He painted the *Mona Lisa* and the fresco *The Last Supper*.

- My hundreds and tens digits are consecutive integers with a sum of 9.
- My units digit is $\frac{1}{2}$ of my hundreds digit.
- Since the sum of my digits is 12, my date is divisible by 3; but it is also divisible by 2 and 6.

What year am I?

April 16

On April 16 of this year, aviation pioneer Wilbur Wright was born in Milville, Indiana.

- My hundreds, tens, and units digits are consecutive integers completely out of order.
- My tens digit is $\frac{3}{4}$ of my hundreds digit; both are even numbers.
- The sum of my digits is 22.

   What year am I?

On April 16 of this year, basketball player Kareem Abdul-Jabbar (Lewis Alcindor, Jr.) was born in New York City.

- The two-digit number formed by my tens and units digits is the 15th prime number.
- The sum of all of my digits is 21.

   What year am I?

April 17

On April 17 of this year, Thornton Wilder was born in Madison, Wisconsin. He was an American playwright, novelist, and Pulitzer Prize winner.

- The two-digit number formed by my tens and units digits is the largest two-digit prime number.
- My hundreds digit is one less than my tens digit.

   What year am I?

On April 17 of this year, the 335-year "state of war" that had existed between the Netherlands and the Scilly Isles came to an end. The Dutch ambassador flew to the Scilly Isles to deliver a proclamation terminating the war that had started over 300 years earlier. Though hostilities had ended centuries before, no one had bothered to declare the war over.

- My tens and units digits are consecutive even integers whose product is 48.
- My units digit is a perfect number.
- My units digit is $\frac{2}{3}$ of my hundreds digit.

   What year am I?

April 18

On April 18 of this year, Paul Revere and William Dawes made their "Midnight Ride" to warn American patriots between Boston and Concord of the approach of the British troops.

- My date is divisible by 5.
- The prime factorization of the two-digit number formed by my tens and units digits is 3×5^2.
- The sum of all of my digits is 20.

What year am I?

On April 18 of this year, San Francisco was devastated by earthquake and fire. The business section and about 10,000 acres were destroyed; nearly 4,000 lives were lost.

- My hundreds digit is square; my units digit is perfect.
- The sum of all of my digits is 16.

What year am I?

April 19

On April 19 of this year, the Battle of Lexington began the American Revolutionary War. The first gunfire was called "the shot heard round the world."

- My odd date is divisible by 5.
- My hundreds and tens digits could be the sides of a square with a perimeter of 28.

What year am I?

On April 19 of this year, the American Revolutionary War *ended*. What an amazing coincidence that the war began and ended on the same day!

- My hundreds and tens digits are consecutive integers with a sum of 15.
- My units digit is the smallest single-digit odd prime.

What year am I?

April 20

On April 20 of this year, American sculptor Daniel Chester French was born. He created the Lincoln Memorial.

- My date is divisible by 2, 5, and 10.
- My tens digit is the third prime number.
- The sum of all of my digits is 14.

   What year am I?

On April 20 of this year, Marie and Pierre Curie isolated the element radium. This husband-and-wife team were awarded the Nobel Prize for work with radium and polonium. Later, Marie Curie won a second Nobel Prize for her work in chemistry, making her the first person to win the prize twice. Even more amazing, Marie Curie's daughter, Irene Curie Julio, was also awarded a Nobel Prize.

- My date is divisible by 2, 3, and 6.
- My units digit raised to the third power would be one less than my hundreds digit.
- My tens digit is the additive identity.

   What year am I?

April 21

On April 21 of this year, German educator Friedrich Froebel was born. He started the first kindergarten in Blankenburg, Germany. Froebel also invented a series of toys to stimulate learning. He started the preschool movement in the United States and England.

- My date is divisible by 2, 3, 6, and 9.
- My units digit is $\frac{1}{4}$ of my tens digit.
- The sum of my thousands and hundreds digits is equal to my tens digit.

   What year am I?

On April 21 of this year, English novelist Charlotte Brontë was born. She wrote *Jane Eyre*.

- The two-digit number formed by my tens and units digits is two less than the two-digit number formed by my thousands and hundreds digits; both are even numbers.
- My units digit is $\frac{3}{4}$ of my hundreds digit.
- The sum of all of my digits is 16.

   What year am I?

April 22

On April 22 of this year, the first Earth Day was observed with the message "Give Earth a Chance." Attention was given to the purity of the air, the water, and our living environment.

- The two-digit number formed by my hundreds and tens digits is the largest two-digit prime number.
- My date is divisible by 2, 5, and 10.

What year am I?

On April 22 of this year, Russian revolutionary leader Nikolai Lenin was born. He led the Great October Revolution. When he died, his embalmed body was placed in a glass coffin in Moscow. Millions of visitors go to Moscow's Red Square to view his remains.

- The sum of my thousands and tens digits is equal to my hundreds digit.
- My date is divisible by 2, 5, and 10.
- The sum of all of my digits is 16.

What year am I?

April 23

On April 23 of this year, William Shakespeare was born in Stratford-on-Avon in England. He wrote at least 36 plays and 154 sonnets. Shakespeare also died on the 23rd of April.

- My hundreds, tens, and units digits are consecutive integers, but all in the wrong order; their mean is 5.
- My tens digit is one greater than my hundreds digit and my units digit is one less than my hundreds digit.
- The sum of all of my digits is 16.

What year am I?

On April 23 of this year, Spanish poet, playwright, and novelist Miguel de Cervantes died in Madrid, Spain. This was the same day that William Shakespeare died. Cervantes' greatest literary creation was *Don Quixote*, a novel about the immortal Knight of La Mancha, who protected the rights of the underdog.

- The two-digit number formed by my thousands and hundreds digits is the same as the two-digit number formed by my tens and units digits.
- The two-digit number formed by my tens and units digits is equal to 2^4.

What year am I?

April 24

On April 24 of this year, singer, actress, and producer Barbra Streisand was born in New York City.

- The square root of my tens digit is equal to my units digit.
- The difference between my hundreds and thousands digits is equal to the product of my tens and units digits.
- The sum of my tens and units digits is 6.

What year am I?

On April 24 of this year, the Library of Congress was created by an act of Congress. It is one of the world's great libraries.

- My date is divisible by 2, 3, 4, 5, 6, 8, 10, and 100.
- The sum of all of my digits is 9.

What year am I?

April 25

On April 25 of this year, the first Seeing Eye dog was presented in America. It has been found that a purebred female German shepherd makes the most effective Seeing Eye dog.

- My tens and units digits are consecutive integers whose product is $\frac{2}{3}$ of my hundreds digit.
- My units digit is $\frac{1}{3}$ of my hundreds digit.
- The sum of all of my digits is 15.

What year am I?

On April 25 of this year, inventor Guglielmo Marconi was born in Italy. He invented the wireless telegraph and won a Nobel Prize.

- My units digit is 50% of my hundreds digit.
- My hundreds and tens digits could be the sides of a rectangle with an area of 56.
- The sum of all of my digits is 20.

What year am I?

April 26

On April 26 of this year, seismologist Charles Francis Richter was born near Hamilton, Ohio. Richter developed the earthquake magnitude scale that is named after him. If an earthquake has a magnitude of 1 on the Richter scale, it has a power of 10^1; a magnitude of 5 is equal to 10^5 and is 10,000 times more powerful.

- My date is 1.9×10^3 in scientific notation.
- The sum of all of my digits is 10.

What year am I?

On April 26 of this year, American artist and naturalist John James Audubon was born in Haiti. Audubon was an ornithologist. (Do you know what that means?)

- My date is divisible by 3 and 5.
- My hundreds and tens digits are consecutive integers whose sum is 15.
- My hundreds and units digits are prime numbers.

What year am I?

April 27

On April 27 of this year, Ulysses S. Grant was born in Point Pleasant, Ohio. The 18th president of the United States, Grant commanded the Union armies and received General Lee's surrender at Appomattox, Virginia.

- My tens and units digits could be the sides of a square; they are the cube root of my hundreds digit.
- The sum of all of my digits is 13.

What year am I?

On April 27 of this year, American cartoonist Walter Lantz was born. He created Woody Woodpecker.

- My date is divisible by 2, 4, 5, 10, 25, and 100.
- The sum of my digits is 10.

What year am I?

April 28

On April 28 of this year, the most famous of all naval mutinies occurred on board H.M.S. *Bounty*. The captain of the *Bounty* was William Bligh, a mean-spirited but able seaman. Fletcher Christian, leader of the mutiny, set Bligh and 18 of his loyal followers adrift in a 23-foot open boat. They survived a 47-day voyage of more than 3,600 miles. Christian set up a colony on an uninhabited island in the Pacific, and the mutineers remained undiscovered for over 18 years.

- My hundreds, tens, and units digits are consecutive integers with a mean of 8.
- My hundreds digit is odd and prime, but my units digit is only odd.

What year am I?

On April 28 of this year, James Monroe was born in Virginia. He was the fifth president of the United States and the author of the Monroe Doctrine.

- My date is divisible by 2, 3, and 6.
- My hundreds and tens digits are consecutive odd integers in reverse order; both are prime.
- The sum of my thousands and hundreds digits is equal to my units digit.

What year am I?

April 29

On April 29 of this year, American newspaper editor and publisher William Randolph Hearst was born in San Francisco, California.

- My date is divisible by 3 and 9.
- My units digit is $\frac{1}{2}$ of my tens digit.
- My tens digit is $\frac{3}{4}$ of my hundreds digit.

What year am I?

On April 29 of this year, African-American musician Duke Ellington was born. He is one of the founders of big band jazz.

- My tens and units digits could be the sides of a square with a perimeter of 36.
- The sum of all of my digits is 27.

What year am I?

April 30

On April 30 of this year, German mathematician Carl Friedrich Gauss was born. He is considered one of the greatest mathematicians of all time. When young Gauss was told by his teacher to find the sum of all the numbers from 1 to 100, he found the answer in a flash by recognizing this pattern:

$$1 + 2 + 3 + \ldots\ldots\ldots\ldots\ldots + 98 + 99 + 100$$
$$1 + 100 = 101; 2 + 99 = 101; 3 + 98 = 101$$

Since there are 50 pairs of 101, the sum is 101×50.

- My hundreds, tens, and units digits could be the sides of a cube with a volume of 343 cubic units.
- The sum of all of my digits is 22.

What year am I?

On April 30 of this year, Louisiana became the 18th state of the United States.

- The two-digit number formed by my tens and units digits could be the area of a rectangle with a length of 3 and a width of 4.
- My hundreds digit is equal to $\sqrt{64}$.

What year am I?

May 1

On May 1 of this year, French chemist Louis-Marie Chardonnet was born. He invented rayon, the first artificial fiber used in making cloth.

- My tens and units digits are both odd; my units digit is 300% of my tens digit.
- The sum of my thousands and hundreds digits is equal to my units digit.
- The sum of all of my digits is 21.

What year am I?

On May 1 of this year, Mary Harris Jones (Mother Jones) was born in Cork, Ireland. After the death of her husband and four children in the Memphis yellow fever epidemic, she devoted her energies and her life to organizing and advancing the cause of labor in the United States.

- My date is divisible by 2, 3, 5, and 10.
- My tens digit is $\frac{1}{3}$ the sum of my hundreds and thousands digits.
- The sum of all of my digits is 12.

What year am I?

May 2

On May 2 of this year, baseball great Stan Musial set a record by hitting five home runs on one day in two games.

- My hundreds digit is a factor of the two-digit number formed by my tens and units digits.
- My tens and units digits are consecutive integers (in reverse order); if they were the sides of a rectangle, its area would be 20 and its perimeter would be 18.

What year am I?

On May 2 of this year, Catherine the Great was born. She was the empress of Russia from 1762 to 1796.

- The sum of my hundreds and tens digits is equal to my units digit.
- The two-digit number formed by my tens and units digits is the 10th prime number.

What year am I?

May 3

On May 3 of this year, Golda Meir was born in Milwaukee, Wisconsin. She became a prime minister of Israel.

- The three-digit number formed by my hundreds, tens, and units digits is a palindrome with a sum of 25.
- My hundreds and units digits are cubic numbers; my tens digit is a square number.

What year am I?

On May 3 of this year, Henry M. Robert was born. He wrote *Robert's Rules of Order,* which is used as a standard parliamentary guide.

- The two-digit number formed by my tens and units digits is the 12th prime number.
- The sum of my thousands and hundreds digits is one less than the sum of my tens and units digits.
- The sum of all of my digits is 19.

What year am I?

730 Daily Math Warm-ups

May 4

On May 4 of this year, American educator Horace Mann was born in Franklin, Massachusetts. Mann was the founder of Westfield State College and editor of the influential *Common School Journal.* He became known as the "Father of Public Education" in the United States.

- My units digit is $\frac{2}{3}$ of my tens digit.
- My prime hundreds digit is one greater than my units digit.

What year am I?

On May 4 of this year, four students were killed by the National Guard when they participated in an antiwar demonstration on the campus of Kent State University in Ohio. The students were Allison Krause, 19; Sandra Lee Scheuer, 20; Jeffrey Glenn Miller, 20; and William Schroeder, 19.

- My date is divisible by 10.
- My hundreds and tens digits are odd integers whose sum is 16.
- My tens digit is a prime number.

What year am I?

May 5

On May 5 of this year, forces led by General Ignacio Zaragoza defeated the French troops of Napoleon III at the Battle of Puebla. The Mexican holiday Cinco de Mayo commemorates the victory, which is celebrated by Mexicans everywhere with parades and festivals.

- My tens digit is $\frac{3}{4}$ of my hundreds digit.
- My units digit is $\frac{1}{3}$ of my tens digit.
- The sum of all of my digits is 17.

What year am I?

On May 5 of this year, Gwendolyn Brooks became the first black American to win the Pulitzer Prize.

- My date is divisible by 10.
- My tens digit is $\frac{1}{2}$ the sum of my hundreds and thousands digits.
- The sum of all of my digits is 15.

What year am I?

May 6

On May 6 of this year, baseball player Willie Mays was born in Fairfield, Alabama.

- If my hundreds digit were $\frac{1}{3}$ its size, my date would be a palindrome.
- The two-digit number formed by my tens and units digits is the 11th prime number.
- The sum of all of my digits is 14.

What year am I?

On May 6 of this year, the dirigible *Hindenburg* exploded as it approached its mooring in New Jersey after a transatlantic crossing. Thirty-six of its ninety-seven passengers and crew died.

- Both my tens and units digits are prime numbers; my units digit is four greater than my tens digit.
- My tens digit is $\frac{1}{3}$ of my hundreds digit.
- The sum of all of my digits is 20.

What year am I?

May 7

On May 7 of this year, Russian composer Pyotr Tchaikovsky was born. He wrote the *1812 Overture* (played on July 4), and the ballets *Sleeping Beauty*, *Swan Lake*, and *The Nutcracker Suite*.

- My date is even and divisible by 5.
- My tens digit is 50% of my hundreds digit.
- The sum of all of my digits is 13.

What year am I?

On May 7 of this year, the British passenger ship *Lusitania* was torpedoed by a German submarine while traveling from New York to England. It was carrying nearly 2,000 passengers; 1,198 lives were lost. Germany had warned President Wilson in advance, claiming that the *Lusitania* was carrying ammunition to England.

- The two-digit number formed by my tens and units digits could be the area of a rectangle with sides of 3 and 5.
- My hundreds digit is a square odd number.

What year am I?

May 8

On May 8 of this year, President Harry S Truman was born in Lamar, Missouri. Truman succeeded to office upon the death of Franklin Delano Roosevelt. He was the ninth (and most recent) president who did not attend college. He once said, "There's nothing new except the history we haven't read." He also had a sign on his desk that read, "The buck stops here."

- If my units digit were $\frac{1}{4}$ of its size, my date would be a palindrome.
- My units digit is 400% of my thousands digit.
- The sum of all of my digits is 21.

What year am I?

On May 8 of this year, Hernando de Soto became the first European to reach the Mississippi River.

- If my tens digit were one greater, my date would be a palindrome.
- The two-digit number formed by my tens and units digits is the 13th prime number.

What year am I?

May 9

On May 9 of this year, the first newspaper cartoon was published in America. (Can you explain the difference between cartoons and comics?)

- The two-digit number formed by my tens and units digits could be the area of a rectangle with a length of 9 and a width of 6.
- My hundreds digit is equal to $\sqrt{49}$.

What year am I?

On May 9 of this year, the North Pole was first viewed from an airplane by American aviators Richard Byrd and Floyd Bennett.

- The two-digit number formed by my tens and units digits could be the perimeter of a rectangle with a length of 8 and a width of 5.
- The sum of all of my digits is 18.

What year am I?

May 10

On May 10 of this year, the Union Pacific and Central Pacific railways were linked at Promontory Point, Utah, by a golden spike. This event has been described as the final link in the ocean-to-ocean railroad.

- My tens digit is 75% of my hundreds digit.
- My tens digit is $66\frac{2}{3}$% of my units digit.
- The sum of all of my digits is 24.

What year am I?

On May 10 of this year, the first planetarium in the United States opened in the city of Chicago. It is called the Adler Planetarium.

- My tens digit is $\frac{1}{3}$ of my hundreds digit.
- My date is divisible by 5 and 10.
- The sum of all of my digits is 13.

What year am I?

May 11

On May 11 of this year, composer Irving Berlin (Israel Baline) was born in Temun, Russia. He immigrated to the United States and wrote hundreds of songs, including "God Bless America" and "I'm Dreaming of a White Christmas."

- My hundreds, tens, and units digits could be the sides of a cube with a volume of 512.
- The sum of all of my digits is 25.

What year am I?

On May 11 of this year, Minnesota was admitted to the United States as the 32nd state.

- My hundreds, tens, and units digits form a palindrome whose sum is 21.
- My tens digit is the third prime number.

What year am I?

May 12

On May 12 of this year, English author Edward Lear was born in Highgate, England. He is remembered for his limericks, published in a book entitled *Book of Nonsense*. Here's an example:

> There was a young poet named Lear
> Who said it is just as I fear
> Five lines are enough
> For this kind of stuff
> Make a limerick each day of the year.

- My date is divisible by 2, 3, 4, and 6.
- My units digit is 25% of my hundreds digit.
- The sum of all of my digits is 12.

What year am I?

On May 12 of this year, English nurse Florence Nightingale was born. She is considered the person most responsible for making nursing the respected profession it is today.

- My hundreds digit is four times the size of my tens digit.
- My date is divisible by 5 and 10.
- The sum of all of my digits is 11.

What year am I?

May 13

On May 13 of this year, Jamestown was settled by the English. It became the first permanent settlement in North America.

- The sum of my thousands and hundreds digits is equal to my units digit.
- My units digit is equal to $\sqrt{49}$.
- The sum of all of my digits is 14.

What year am I?

On May 13 of this year, singer and musician Stevie Wonder (Steveland Morris Hardaway) was born in Saginaw, Michigan.

- If my tens digit were four greater, my date would be a palindrome.
- The two-digit number formed by my tens and units digits is a multiple of 3 and 17.

What year am I?

May 14

On May 14 of this year, Daniel Gabriel Fahrenheit was born in Gdansk, Poland. He introduced the use of mercury in thermometers and greatly increased their accuracy.

- My hundreds, tens, and units digits (all even numbers) form a palindrome whose sum is 20.
- My units digit is $\frac{3}{4}$ of my tens digit.

What year am I?

On May 14 of this year, Israel became an independent nation.

- My tens digit is 50% of my units digit.
- My units digit is a cubic number; my hundreds digit is a square number.
- The sum of all of my digits is 22.

What year am I?

May 15

On May 15 of this year, author Lyman Frank Baum was born in Chittenango, New York. An American newspaperman, Baum wrote the *Wizard of Oz* stories. *The Wonderful World of Oz* was the most famous, but he wrote many other books for children—including more than a dozen about Oz.

- My units digit is $\frac{3}{4}$ of my hundreds digit.
- My tens and units digits are consecutive integers whose sum is 11 and product is 30.

What year am I?

On May 15 of this year, Ellen Church became the first airline stewardess. She was a flight attendant for United Airlines.

- My prime tens digit is the square root of my odd hundreds digit.
- The sum of all of my digits is 13.

What year am I?

May 16

On May 16 of this year, mathematician Maria Gaetana Agnesi was born in Italy. Maria was a gifted child who spoke more than a dozen languages by the age of 9. Her love, however, was mathematics; and even in a time when women were not educated, she became famous for her published books of mathematics.

- The two-digit number formed by my tens and units digits (which is even) is one greater than the two-digit number formed by my thousands and hundreds digits (which is prime).
- The sum of all of my digits is 17.

What year am I?

On May 16 of this year, the first Oscar Awards were presented by the Academy of Motion Picture Arts and Sciences.

- The two-digit number formed by my tens and units digits is the 10th prime number.
- My hundreds, tens, and units digits form a palindrome.
- My date is divisible by 3.

What year am I?

May 17

On May 17 of this year, English physician Edward Jenner was born. He was the originator of the inoculation that we use against smallpox. During the Middle Ages, smallpox epidemics caused the death of millions of people.

- My hundreds digit raised to the second power is equal to the two-digit number formed by my tens and units digits.
- The two-digit number formed by my thousands and hundreds digits is the seventh prime number.

What year am I?

On May 17 of this year, racial segregation was declared unconstitutional by the U.S. Supreme Court in the history-making case *Brown* v. *the Board of Education*.

- The sum of my tens and units digits is equal to my hundreds digit.
- The two-digit number formed by my tens and units digits is a multiple of my hundreds digit.
- The sum of all of my digits is 19.
- My units digit is one less than my tens digit.

What year am I?

May 18

On May 18 of this year, Mount Saint Helens erupted. The eruption of this volcano in south-western Washington blew steam and ashes more than 11 miles into the sky. This was the volcano's first major eruption in over 100 years.

- My date is divisible by 2, 3, 5, 6, 9, and 10.
- The sum of my thousands and tens digits is equal to my hundreds digit.
- The sum of all of my digits is 18.

What year am I?

On May 18 of this year, Pope John Paul II (Karol Wojtyla) was born in Wadowice, Poland. He is the 264th pope of the Roman Catholic Church, the first non-Italian to be elected pope in 456 years, and the first Polish pope ever.

- The two-digit number formed by my tens and units digits is equal to $2^2 \times 5$.
- The sum of all of my digits is 12.

What year am I?

May 19

On May 19 of this year, black civil rights leader Malcolm X (Malcolm Little) was born in Omaha, Nebraska. He changed his name to Malcolm X; he took the letter "X" to replace the family name assigned by white owners to their slaves. He began the Organization of American Unity. He was assassinated in New York City.

- The two-digit number formed by my tens and units digits is equal to 5^2.
- The sum of all of my digits is 17.

What year am I?

On May 19 of this year, the Simplon Tunnel connecting Switzerland and Italy was officially opened.

- My units digit is equal to 3!.
- The two-digit number formed by my thousands and hundreds digits is the largest prime < 20.
- The sum of all of my digits is 16.

What year am I?

May 20

On May 20 of this year, 25-year-old aviator Captain Charles Lindbergh departed from a rainy field in New York at 7:52 A.M. to begin his solitary flight across the Atlantic to Paris. His monoplane was called the *Spirit of St. Louis*; the 3,600-mile flight took almost 39 hours.

- Three times my hundreds digit is equal to the two-digit number formed by my tens and units digits.
- The sum of my tens and units digits is equal to my hundreds digit.
- The sum of all of my digits is 19.

What year am I?

On May 20 of this year, Dolley Madison was born in North Carolina. The wife of our fourth president, James Madison, she played a major role in rescuing many pieces of art and public papers during a fire at the White House.

- The mean of my hundreds, tens, and units digits is 7.
- My tens digit is one less than my hundreds digit; my units digit is one more than my hundreds digit.
- The sum of all of my digits is 22.

What year am I?

May 21

On May 21 of this year, German painter and engraver Albrecht Dürer was born in Nuremberg. He was one of the greatest artists of the Renaissance era.

- The two-digit number formed by my thousands and hundreds digits is equal to twice my prime tens digit.
- If my hundreds digit were three greater, my date would be a palindrome.
- The sum of all of my digits is 13.

What year am I?

On May 21 of this year, the American Red Cross was founded by Clara Barton.

- My date is a palindrome whose sum is 18.

What year am I?

May 22

On May 22 of this year, English author and physician Arthur Conan Doyle was born. He is best known for creating Sherlock Holmes and Dr. Watson.

- My hundreds digit is a cubic number, my units digit is a square number, and my tens digit is a prime number.
- The sum of my thousands and hundreds digits is equal to my units digit.
- The sum of all of my digits is 23.

What year am I?

On May 22 of this year, American race-car driver Janet Guthrie was officially recognized as the first woman to qualify for the Indianapolis 500 race.

- My tens and units digits could be the sides of a square with an area of 49 and a perimeter of 28.
- The sum of all of my digits is 24.

What year am I?

May 23

On May 23 of this year, German physician Friedrich Anton Mesmer was born. He developed a form of hypnotism, which was called "mesmerism" after him, to treat his patients.

- My tens and units digits are consecutive integers whose sum is 7 and whose product is 12.
- Both my hundreds and tens digits are prime numbers.
- The sum of all of my digits is 15.

What year am I?

On May 23 of this year, Arabella Mansfield was born in Iowa. She was the first woman in American to be admitted to the legal profession.

- My hundreds, tens, and units digits are all even numbers.
- My tens digit is $\frac{1}{2}$ of my hundreds digit; my units digit is $1\frac{1}{2}$ times the size of my tens digit.
- The sum of all of my digits is 19.

What year am I?

May 24

On May 24 of this year, the Brooklyn Bridge opened in New York City. The bridge took 14 years to construct and cost over $16 million; it crosses the East River, connecting Manhattan and Brooklyn. The steel suspension bridge, designed by John Roebling, has a span of 1,595 feet.

- My hundreds and tens digits could be the sides of a square with a perimeter of 32.
- My units digit is the smallest odd prime number.

What year am I?

On May 24 of this year, the first major league night baseball game was played. The teams in this game were from Cincinnati and Philadelphia.

- My tens and units digits are consecutive primes.
- The sum of my thousands, tens, and units digits is equal to my hundreds digit.
- My tens digit is $\frac{1}{3}$ of my hundreds digit.

What year am I?

May 25

On May 25 of this year, aeronautical engineer Igor Sikorsky was born in Kiev, Russia. He is best remembered for the development of the first successful helicopter. He also pioneered multiengine airplanes.

- My tens and units digits are consecutive integers with a sum of 17.
- My hundreds and tens digits could be the sides of a square with an area of 64.

What year am I?

On May 25 of this year, musician and composer Miles Davis was born in Alton, Illinois.

- My units digit is $\frac{2}{3}$ of my hundreds digit.
- My tens digit is $\frac{1}{3}$ of my units digit.
- My date is divisible by 2, 3, 6, and 9.

What year am I?

May 26

On May 26 of this year, Dr. Sally Kristen Ride was born in Encino, California. One of seven women in the U.S. astronaut corps and the first American woman in space, she is married to another astronaut, Steve Hawley. Her flight aboard the space shuttle *Challenger*, a six-day mission, was called a "nearly perfect mission."

- If my tens digit were four greater, my date would be a palindrome.
- The sum of all of my digits is 16.

What year am I?

On May 26 of this year, actor John Wayne (Marion Michael Morrison) was born in Winterset, Iowa. His advice on acting was "Talk low, talk slow, and don't say too much."

- My units digit is the largest single-digit prime.
- My tens digit is the additive identity element.
- The sum of all of my digits is 17.

What year am I?

May 27

On May 27 of this year, American scientist and author Rachel Carson was born in Springdale, Pennsylvania. She was the author of the book *Silent Spring,* which detailed the dangers of the overuse of pesticides and chemicals to our environment and wildlife.

- The two-digit number formed by my thousands and hundreds digits is the eighth prime number.
- My units digit is the largest prime number < 10.
- The sum of all of my digits is 17.

What year am I?

On May 27 of this year, the Golden Gate Bridge was opened in San Francisco, California.

- My tens digit is $\frac{1}{3}$ of my hundreds digit.
- Twice my tens digit plus one is equal to my units digit.
- The sum of all of my digits is 20.

What year am I?

May 28

On May 28 of this year, American athlete James Francis Thorpe was born near Prague, Oklahoma. Thorpe, a Native American, won the pentathlon and decathlon events in the 1912 Olympics and later became a professional baseball and football player.

- My hundreds, tens, and units digits could be the sides of a cube with a volume of 512.

What year am I?

On May 28 of this year, the Dionne quintuplets (Marie, Cecile, Yvonne, Emilie, and Annette) were born in Ontario, Canada. They were the first quints known to survive for more than a few hours after birth.

- My tens digit is $\frac{1}{3}$ of my hundreds digit.
- My units digit is an even square number that is one greater than my tens digit.
- The sum of all of my digits is 17.

What year am I?

May 29

On May 29 of this year, John Fitzgerald Kennedy was born in Brookline, Massachusetts. The 35th president of the United States, Kennedy was the youngest man ever to be elected president, the first Roman Catholic, and the first president ever to have served in the Navy. He was the fourth president to be killed by an assassin, and the second to be buried in Arlington National Cemetery.

- The two-digit number formed by my tens and units digits and the two-digit number formed by my thousands and hundreds digits are consecutive odd numbers (in reverse order).
- The sum of all of my digits is 18.

What year am I?

On May 29 of this year, comedian Bob Hope (Leslie Townes) was born in Eltham, England.

- My units digit is $33\frac{1}{3}$ % of my hundreds digit.
- My tens digit is the additive identity.
- The sum of all of my digits is 13.

What year am I?

May 30

On May 30 of this year, Mel Blanc was born in San Francisco, California. His was the voice of Bugs Bunny and many other cartoon characters.

- My hundreds digit is a square number; my units digit is a cubic number; their difference is one.
- The sum of my digits is 18.

What year am I?

On May 30 of this year, Saint Joan of Arc was burned at the stake. The Maid of Orleans was a French heroine who led the French army against the invading English. She was captured and died at the age of 19. Almost 500 years later, she was raised to sainthood.

- The two-digit number formed by my thousands and hundreds digits is a multiple of 7 and 2.
- My tens digit is the smallest odd prime number.
- The sum of all of my digits is 9.

What year am I?

May 31

On May 31 of this year, actor Clint Eastwood was born in San Francisco, California. He is famous for his statement "Make my day!" in the movie *Dirty Harry*.

- My tens digit raised to the second power is equal to my hundreds digit.
- My date is divisible by 2, 5, and 10.
- The sum of all of my digits is 13.

What year am I?

On May 31 of this year, American poet Walt Whitman was born. He wrote *Leaves of Grass*.

- The two-digit number formed by my thousands and hundreds digits and the two-digit number formed by my tens and units digits are consecutive integers.
- My hundreds digit is a cubic number; my units digit is a square number.
- The sum of all of my digits is 19.

What year am I?

June 1

On June 1 of this year, Kentucky became the 15th state to be admitted to the United States.

- My hundreds and tens digits are consecutive odd integers whose sum is 16 and whose product is 63.
- My units digit is $\sqrt[3]{8}$.
- The sum of my digits is 19.

What year am I?

On June 1 of this year, the first U.S. earthquake to be described in writing occurred in Plymouth, Massachusetts. Governor William Bradford recorded the event for history by saying, ". . . ye earth shooke with ye violence as they could not stand without catching hold of ye posts . . ."

- My date is divisible by at least 2, 3, 6, 9, and 18.
- My hundreds digit is twice the size of my tens digit but two less than my units digit.
- The sum of all of my digits is 18.

What year am I?

June 2

On June 2 of this year, Native Americans were granted citizenship by Congress.

- The two-digit number formed by my tens and units digits is a multiple of 2, 3, 4, 6, and 12.
- My hundreds digit minus one is equal to twice my units digit and four times my tens digit.
- The sum of all of my digits is 16.

What year am I?

On June 2 of this year, actress Sally Kellerman was born in Long Beach, California. (Can you name some of her movies?)

- My hundreds digit is a factor of the two-digit number formed by my tens and units digits.
- My tens digit is 50% of my units digit but $\frac{1}{3}$ of my hundreds digit.
- The sum of all of my digits is 19.

What year am I?

June 3

On June 3 of this year, the famous poem "Casey at the Bat" was first printed in the *San Francisco Examiner*. It was written by Ernest Thayer.

- My hundreds, tens, and units digits could be the sides of a cube with a volume of 512 cubic units.
- My date is divisible by 2.
- The sum of all of my digits is 25.

What year am I?

On June 3 of this year, Sally Jan Priesand was ordained at the Stephen Wise Free Synagogue in New York City as the first woman rabbi.

- My date is divisible by 2 and 4.
- The sum of my tens and units digits is equal to my hundreds digit.
- My hundreds digit could be the area of a square with a side of 3.

What year am I?

June 4

On June 4 of this year, Marie Thible of Lyons, France, became the first woman in history to fly in a balloon. The balloon reached a height of over 8,000 feet, and the flight lasted about 45 minutes.

- The sum of my thousands and hundreds digits is equal to my tens digit.
- My date is divisible by 2, 4, and 8, at least.
- My units digit is $\frac{1}{2}$ my tens digit.
- The sum of all of my digits is 20.

What year am I?

On June 4 of this year, George III was born. He was the English king against whom the American Revolution was fought.

- The sum of my thousands and hundreds digits is equal to my units digit.
- My tens digit is the smallest odd prime number.
- My units digit could be the volume of a cube with sides of 2 units.
- The sum of all of my digits is 19.

What year am I?

June 5

On June 5 of this year, Senator Robert Kennedy was shot while campaigning for the Democratic presidential nomination in Los Angeles, California. He was shot by Sirhan Sirhan and died the following day.

- My date is divisible by at least 2, 3, 4, 6, and 12.
- My tens digit is a perfect number.
- The sum of my thousands and units digits is equal to my hundreds digit.
- The sum of all of my digits is 24.

What year am I?

On June 5 of this year, the Greek philosopher Socrates was born. Socrates' ideas and teachings were written down by his student Plato. (We need to write "B.C." after his birth date.)

- My hundreds digit is an even square number; my units digit is an odd square number.
- My tens digit is 150% of my hundreds digit; my units digit is 150% of my tens digit.
- The sum of all of my digits is 19.

What year am I?

June 6

On June 6 of this year, the U.S. armed forces landed on the beaches of Normandy, France. Over 9,500 Americans died during the entire campaign and are buried in the American cemetery on the beach. This day is called D day.

- My tens and units digits could be the sides of a square with both a perimeter and an area of 16.
- The sum of all of my digits is 18.

What year am I?

On June 6 of this year, American patriot Nathan Hale was born. He was captured and sentenced to die; his dying words were, "I only regret that I have but one life to give for my country."

- My date is divisible by 3, 5, and 9.
- My tens and units digits could be the sides of a square with an area of 25 and a perimeter of 20.
- My hundreds digit is the largest single-digit prime number.

What year am I?

June 7

On June 7 of this year, French artist Paul Gauguin was born in Paris. He moved to Tahiti, where he did most of his work.

- My hundreds, tens, and units digits form a palindrome with a sum of 20.
- My tens digit is $\frac{1}{2}$ of my units digit.
- My date is divisible by at least 2, 3, 4, 6, and 8.

  What year am I?

On June 7 of this year, American writer Gwendolyn Brooks was born. She was named Poet Laureate of Illinois and was the first black to win the Pulitzer Prize for poetry. Her book *Bronzeville Boys and Girls* is a collection of poems about children living in American inner cities.

- The two-digit number formed by my tens and units digits is the seventh prime number.
- The two-digit number formed by my thousands and hundreds digits is the eighth prime number.
- My date is divisible by 3 and 9.

  What year am I?

June 8

On June 8 of this year, American architect Frank Lloyd Wright was born in Wisconsin. He believed that buildings should reflect their surroundings.

- My hundreds, tens, and units digits are consecutive integers in the wrong order.
- My hundreds and tens digits are even numbers; my units digit is a prime number.
- The sum of all of my digits is 22.

  What year am I?

On June 8 of this year, Ives McGaffrey patented the first suction-type vacuum cleaner.

- My hundred and tens digits are even; my tens digit is $\frac{3}{4}$ of my hundreds digit.
- My units digit is an odd number and is 150% of my tens digit.
- The sum of my thousands and hundreds digits is equal to my units digit.

  What year am I?

June 9

On June 9 of this year, cartoon character Donald Duck was "born" at Walt Disney's studio.

- My tens and units digits are consecutive integers whose sum is 7 and product is 12.
- My tens digit is $\frac{1}{3}$ of my hundreds digit.
- The sum of all of my digits is 17.

What year am I?

On June 9 of this year, American composer Cole Porter was born in Indiana. He wrote hundreds of songs, including "Anything Goes," "I Get a Kick Out of You," and "Just One of Those Things."

- My hundreds and tens digits are consecutive integers; if they were the sides of a rectangle, its area would be 72 square units.
- My units digit is $\frac{1}{3}$ of my tens digit.

What year am I?

June 10

On June 10 of this year, silversmith John Hull opened the first mint in America in defiance of British law. The first coin he made was the Pine Tree Shilling.

- My date is divisible by 2 and 4.
- My hundreds digit is a perfect number; the tens digit is one less.
- The sum of all of my digits is 14.

What year am I?

On June 10 of this year, actress Hattie McDaniel was born in Wichita, Kansas. She was the first African American to win an Academy Award; she received it for her performance in *Gone With the Wind*.

- My hundreds and tens digits are the same even number.
- My tens and units digits are consecutive integers whose sum is 17; their product is 72.

What year am I?

June 11

On June 11 of this year, Jacques-Yves Cousteau was born. He was a Frenchman who explored the oceans, making films and writing about his adventures.

- My date is divisible by 2, 5, and 10.
- My thousands, hundreds, and tens digits form a palindrome with a sum of 11.

What year am I?

On June 11 of this year, Jeannette Rankin was born in Missoula, Montana. She was the first woman to be elected to the U.S. Congress. A feminist and a pacifist, she was the only member of Congress to vote against a declaration of war with Japan.

- My date is divisible by 2, 5, and 10.
- My hundreds and tens digits could be the sides of a square with a perimeter of 24 and an area of 64.
- The sum of all of my digits is 17.

What year am I?

June 12

On June 12 of this year, George Herbert Bush was born in Milton, Massachusetts. He was the 41st president of the United States.

- My tens and units digits are consecutive even integers whose sum is 6 and product is 8.
- My hundreds digit is equal to $\sqrt{81}$.
- My units digit is 200% of my tens digit.

What year am I?

On June 12 of this year, Anne Frank was born. She was the young Jewish girl who kept a diary while hiding in an attic to avoid being captured by Nazis. The diary was later published as a book called *Anne Frank: Diary of a Young Girl*.

- My hundreds, tens, and units digits form a palindrome with a sum of 20.
- My tens digit is the only even prime number.
- The sum of all of my digits is 21.

What year am I?

June 13

On June 13 of this year, African American civil rights leader Medgar Wiley Evers was assassinated by Byron de la Beckwith. Evers was active in seeking integration of schools and registering blacks in the South to vote.

- My tens digit is $\frac{2}{3}$ of my hundreds digit; my units digit is $\frac{1}{3}$ of my hundreds digit.
- The sum of all of my digits is 19.

   What year am I?

On June 13 of this year (B.C.), Alexander the Great died. He was the King of Macedonia.

- My hundreds, tens, and units digits are a palindrome whose sum is 8.
- All of my digits are prime numbers, although two are odd and one is even.

   What year am I?

June 14

On June 14 of this year, American editor John Bartlett was born in Plymouth, Massachusetts. Although he had no formal education, he compiled one of the most used reference works in the English language: Bartlett's *Familiar Quotations*.

- My date is divisible by 2, 5, and 10.
- My tens digit is 25% of my hundreds digit.
- The sum of all of my digits is 11.

   What year am I?

On June 14 of this year, author Harriet Beecher Stowe was born in Litchfield, Connecticut. Her antislavery novel *Uncle Tom's Cabin* created a storm of controversy and had political impact without parallel in American literature.

- The two-digit number formed by my tens and units digits is the smallest two-digit prime number.
- My hundreds digit is a cubic number.
- The sum of all of my digits is 11.

   What year am I?

June 15

On June 15 of this year, Benjamin Franklin conducted his experiment with a kite to prove that lightning contained electricity.

- My date is divisible by 2.
- The sum of my tens and units digits is equal to my hundreds digit.
- My hundreds digit is the largest single-digit prime number.
- My units digit is the only even prime number.

What year am I?

On June 15 of this year, King John signed the Magna Carta. This declaration is considered to be one of the most important documents in the history of humanity's search for liberty and freedom. Four copies have survived through the years.

- My date is divisible by 3, 5, and 9.
- The two-digit number formed by my thousands and hundreds digits is three less than the two-digit number formed by my tens and units digits.
- The sum of all of my digits is 9.

What year am I?

June 16

On June 16 of this year, John Howard Griffen was born in Dallas, Texas. Griffen, an author and photographer concerned about racial problems in the United States, blackened his skin using chemicals and ultraviolet light. He traveled through the South keeping a journal of his experiences. The journal became his best-known book *Black Like Me*.

- My date is divisible by 2, 3, 5, 6, and 10.
- My tens digit is twice my thousands digit.
- My hundreds digit is an odd square number.

What year am I?

On June 16 of this year, the Russian spacecraft *Vostok VI* carried the first woman into space. Valentina Tereshkova piloted the 10,300-pound vessel during a 70-hour flight that orbited the earth 48 times.

- My prime units digit is $\frac{1}{2}$ of my tens digit and $\frac{1}{3}$ of my hundreds digit.
- The sum of my units and tens digits is equal to my hundreds digit.
- The sum of all of my digits is 19.

What year am I?

June 17

On June 17 of this year, the Battle of Bunker Hill began. This date is celebrated as a legal holiday in Suffolk County in Massachusetts, where the battle took place.

- My hundreds and tens digits could be the sides of a square with a perimeter of 28 and an area of 49.
- My date is divisible by 5 but not by 10.

What year am I?

On June 17 of this year, Russian composer Igor Stravinsky was born near Leningrad. His many well-known compositions include *The Firebird* and *Petrushka.*

- My date is an even number.
- My units digit raised to the third power is equal to my tens digit.
- My tens and hundreds digits could be the sides of a square with a perimeter of 32 and an area of 64.

What year am I?

June 18

On June 18 of this year, Sally Ride became the first American woman in space. She functioned as the mission specialist on a six-day flight of the space shuttle *Challenger.*

- My units digit is $33\frac{1}{3}\%$ of my hundreds digit.
- The sum of my thousands and tens digits is equal to my hundreds digit.
- The sum of all of my digits is 21.

What year am I?

On June 18 of this year, Paul McCartney was born in Liverpool, England. He was a vocalist and composer for the Beatles.

- My units digit is 50% of my tens digit.
- If my hundreds and units digits were the sides of a rectangle, its perimeter would be 22 and its area would be 18.
- The sum of all of my digits is 16.

What year am I?

June 19

On June 19 of this year, the lasagna-loving cartoon cat "Garfield" was "born."

- My hundreds, tens, and units digits are consecutive integers but in a mixed-up order; their sum is 24.
- My tens digit is the largest single-digit prime number.
- The sum of my thousands and units digits is equal to my hundreds digit.

What year am I?

On June 19 of this year, French physicist and mathematician Blaise Pascal was born. Among his many accomplishments was the famous triangle that bears his name. (Try to find number patterns in Pascal's triangle.)

- The two-digit number formed by my tens and units digits is the ninth prime number.
- My hundreds digit is twice my units digit but three times my tens digit.

What year am I?

June 20

On June 20 of this year, the design for the Great Seal of the United States was presented to Congress by Charles Thomson. It was adopted on the same day.

- My hundreds and tens digits are consecutive integers with a sum of 15 and a product of 56.
- My units digit is 25% of my tens digit.
- The sum of all of my digits is 18.

What year am I?

On June 20 of this year, Caroline Willard Baldwin became the first woman to earn a doctor of science degree. She attended Cornell University in Ithaca, New York.

- My date is divisible by 5 but not by 10.
- The sum of my thousands and hundreds digits is equal to my tens digit.
- The sum of all of my digits is 23.

What year am I?

June 21

On June 21 of this year, Daniel Carter Beard was born. He was the founder of the Boy Scouts of America. A naturalist, he founded the organization to promote an appreciation of the outdoors.

- My date is divisible by 2, 5, and 10.
- The sum of my hundreds and tens digits is the sixth prime number.
- Only my tens digit is a prime number.

What year am I?

On June 21 of this year, the wheat reaper was patented. Before this invention, only about 3 acres of wheat could be harvested each day; with the reaper, about 15 could be harvested. (What percent of increase does this represent?)

- The two-digit number formed by my tens and units digits is a multiple of the seventh prime number.
- If my tens and units digits were the sides of a rectangle, its area would be 12 and its perimeter would be 14.
- The sum of all of my digits is 16.

What year am I?

June 22

On June 22 of this year, the United States Department of Justice was established. This department is headed by the attorney general.

- My date is divisible by 2, 5, and 10.
- The sum of my thousands and tens digits is equal to my hundreds digit.
- The sum of all of my digits is 16.

What year am I?

On June 22 of this year, American aviator and author Anne Morrow Lindbergh was born. In *Gift from the Sea,* she wrote, "By and large, mothers and housewives are the only workers who do not have regular time off."

- My tens digit is the additive identity element.
- Both my hundreds and units digits are odd, but only the units digit is prime.
- The sum of my thousands and hundreds digits is three greater than my units digit.

What year am I?

June 23

On June 23 of this year, director and choreographer Bob Fosse was born in Chicago, Illinois. He was the only director in history to win an Oscar, an Emmy, and a Tony for his work. He choreographed and directed many plays, including *Sweet Charity, Pippin, Pajama Game,* and *Damn Yankees.* His films included *Cabaret* and *All That Jazz.*

- The two-digit number formed by my tens and units digits is a multiple of my hundreds digit.
- My hundreds digit is equal to 3^2.
- The sum of all of my digits is 19.
- My units digit is the largest single-digit prime number.

   What year am I?

On June 23 of this year, Christopher Sholes patented the first typewriter.

- My hundreds, tens, and units digits form a palindrome of even numbers; my hundreds and units digits are cubic numbers, my tens is perfect.
- The sum of the digits of this palindrome is 22.

   What year am I?

June 24

On June 24 of this year, the Berlin Airlift began. During the Cold War, the Soviet Union blocked land access to Berlin. The United States flew in 1.6 million tons of food and supplies to the 2.25 million people of Berlin.

- The three-digit number formed by my hundreds, tens, and units digits is a palindrome consisting of only square numbers; the hundreds and units digits are odd, the tens is even.
- The sum of the palindrome is 22.

   What year am I?

On June 24 of this year, the first reported sighting of a UFO (an unidentified flying object or flying saucer) was reported. Kenneth Arnold said it was flying over Mount Rainier in Washington.

- The two-digit number formed by my tens and units digits is the 15th prime number.
- My hundreds digit could be the area of a square whose sides measure 3.
- The sum of all of my digits is 21.

   What year am I?

June 25

On June 25 of this year, CBS broadcast the first color television program. The four-hour program was carried on stations in New York, Baltimore, Philadelphia, Boston, and Washington, although color sets were not available to the public at that time.

- If my tens digit were four greater, my date would be a palindrome with a sum of 20.
- Only my tens digit is a prime number.

What year am I?

On June 25 of this year, English author George Orwell was born. Among his books were *Animal Farm* and *1984*.

- My units digit is $\frac{1}{3}$ of my hundreds digit.
- My tens digit is the additive identity element.

What year am I?

June 26

On June 26 of this year, American author Pearl Buck was born. A noted authority on China, she won the Nobel Prize for her book *The Good Earth*.

- My units digit is 25% or $\frac{1}{4}$ of my hundreds digit.
- My hundreds and tens digits are consecutive integers with a sum of 17 and a product of 72.

What year am I?

On June 26 of this year, the first bicycle was patented.

- The two-digit number formed by my thousands and hundreds digits is one less than the two-digit number formed by my tens and units digits; they are consecutive two-digit numbers with a sum of 37.

What year am I?

June 27

On June 27 of this year, Helen Keller was born in Tuscumbia, Alabama. She was blind and deaf from the age of 19 months, but was taught by Anne Sullivan to communicate. She once said, "To be blind is bad, but it is worse to have eyes and not see."

- If my units digit were one greater, my date would be a palindrome with a sum of 18.
- My date is divisible by 2, 5, and 10.

What year am I?

On June 27 of this year, the song "Happy Birthday to You" was composed by a school teacher named Mildred Hill. Although the author is believed to have earned very little from the song, it later generated about $1 million a year for the owner of the copyright. It is still under copyright, but will enter the public domain in 2010.

- My tens and units digits are odd numbers; if they were the sides of a rectangle its area would be 45 and its perimeter would be 28.
- My tens digit is a prime number; it is three less than my hundreds digit.

What year am I?

June 28

On June 28 of this year, Flemish painter Peter Paul Rubens was born.

- My hundreds and tens digits are consecutive odd integers which are also prime numbers.
- My tens and units digits could be the sides of a square; its area would be 49 and its perimeter would be 28.

What year am I?

On June 28 of this year, American composer Richard Rodgers was born. He wrote the music for several shows, including *Oklahoma!* and *South Pacific*.

- My date is divisible by 2, 3, and 6.
- My units digit is the only even prime number.
- The sum of all of my digits is only 12.

What year am I?

June 29

On June 29 of this year, George Washington Goethals was born in Brooklyn, New York. He served as chief engineer of the Panama Canal.

- My hundreds, tens, and units digits form a palindrome; my tens digit is the third prime number.
- If my hundreds and units digits were the sides of a square, its perimeter would be 32.
- The sum of all of my digits is 22.

What year am I?

On June 29 of this year, American surgeon William James Mayo was born in Le Seuer, Minnesota. He was one of the founders of the Mayo Foundation.

- If my tens digit were two greater, my date would form a palindrome.
- My tens digit is a perfect number.
- The sum of all of my digits is 16.

What year am I?

June 30

On June 30 of this year, Charles Blondin (whose real name was Jean François Gravelet) walked across Niagara Falls on a tightrope. More than 25,000 people watched the five-minute walk.

- The sum of my thousands and hundreds digits is equal to my units digit.
- My hundreds digit is a cubic number; my units digit is a square number.
- Twice my prime tens digit is equal to the sum of my thousands and units digits.

What year am I?

On June 30 of this year, the soap opera *The Guiding Light* was introduced on TV. It holds the record for the longest-lasting daytime show and longest-lasting series.

- Both my tens and units digits are prime numbers, but one is even and the other is odd.
- One more than twice my units digit is equal to my tens digit.
- The sum of my thousands and hundreds digits is equal to the product of my tens and units digits.

What year am I?

July 1

On July 1 of this year, the Battle of Gettysburg began in Pennsylvania. It was one of the Civil War's most crucial battles. General Robert E. Lee was defeated and retreated back to Virginia.

- The sum of my thousands and hundreds digits is equal to the sum of my tens and units digits.
- My units digit is $\frac{1}{2}$ of my tens digit.
- My tens digit is $\frac{3}{4}$ of my hundreds digit.
- My date is divisible by 3, 6, and 9.

What year am I?

On July 1 of this year, German mathematician and philosopher Gottfried Leibniz was born. Leibniz was known for his work in calculus.

- My hundreds, tens, and units digits form an even palindrome with a sum of 16.
- My tens and units digits are consecutive even integers with a product of 24.
- The sum of all of my digits is 17.

What year am I?

July 2

On July 2 of this year, Thurgood Marshall was born in Baltimore, Maryland. He was the first black American to serve on the Supreme Court. His greatest victory came when the Supreme Court declared the "separate but equal" system of racial segregation in the public schools violated our Constitution. He served for 24 years on the Supreme Court.

- My date is divisible by 2, 3, 4, 6, and 9.
- The sum of my thousands and units digits is equal to my hundreds digit.
- My tens digit is the additive identity.

What year am I?

On July 2 of this year, Dave Thomas was born in Camden, New Jersey. He is the founder of Wendy's restaurants. (Have you seen his commercials?)

- My hundreds digit is three times the size of my tens digit.
- The sum of my thousands and units digits is equal to my tens digit.
- The sum of all of my digits is 15.

What year am I?

July 3

On July 3 of this year, Idaho became the 43rd state to be admitted to the United States.

- My date is divisible by 2, 5, and 10.
- My hundreds and tens digits are consecutive integers with a sum of 17 and a product of 72.
- The sum of my thousands and hundreds digits is equal to my tens digit.

What year am I?

On July 3 of this year, American playwright and composer George M. Cohan was born. Cohan's love of America is apparent in two of the songs he wrote: "You're a Grand Old Flag" and "I'm a Yankee Doodle Dandy."

- My hundreds, tens, and units digits form an even palindrome with a sum of 23.
- The sum of my thousands and tens digits is equal to my units digit.

What year am I?

July 4

On July 4 of this year, Katherine Lee Bates published "America the Beautiful." She was a Wellesley College professor.

- My date is divisible by 5 but not 10.
- My hundreds and tens digits are consecutive integers with a sum of 17 and a product of 72.
- The sum of all of my digits is 23.

What year am I?

On July 4 of this year, American songwriter Stephen Foster was born in Lawrenceville, Pennsylvania. He wrote almost 200 songs, including "Oh Suzanna," "Camptown Races," "Old Folks at Home," and "Beautiful Dreamer."

- My tens digit is $\frac{1}{3}$ of my units digit but only $\frac{1}{4}$ of my hundreds digit.
- The sum of my tens and units digits is equal to my hundreds digit.
- My units digit is a perfect number.

What year am I?

July 5

On July 5 of this year, baseball player Richard "Goose" Gossage was born in Colorado Springs, Colorado.

- If my tens digit were four greater, my date would be a palindrome.
- The two-digit number formed by my tens and units digits is a multiple of 17.
- The sum of all of my digits is 16.

What year am I?

On July 5 of this year, P.T. Barnum was born. He was the founder of one of America's most famous circuses. He once said, "There's a sucker born every minute."

- My date is divisible by 2, 5, and 10.
- The three-digit number formed by my thousands, hundreds, and tens digits is a palindrome with a sum of 10.

What year am I?

July 6

On July 6 of this year, Cecil Francis Poole became the first African American to be sworn in as a U.S. attorney. He served for the Northern District of California.

- My even tens digit is $\frac{2}{3}$ of my odd hundreds digit.
- If my hundreds digit were three less, my date would be a palindrome.
- The sum of all of my digits is 17.

What year am I?

On July 6 of this year, author Beatrix Potter was born in London, England. She was the creator of the Peter Rabbit stories.

- The two-digit even number formed by my tens and units digits is a multiple of 11.
- My tens digit is 75% of my hundreds digit.
- My hundreds digit is a cubic number; my units digit is a perfect number.

What year am I?

July 7

On July 7 of this year, Russian artist Marc Chagall was born. He is known for his dreamlike images.

- My hundreds and tens digits could be the sides of a square with a perimeter of 32 and an area of 64.
- The sum of my thousands and units digits is equal to my tens digit.
- My date is divisible by 3.

What year am I?

On July 7 of this year, Beatles' drummer Ringo Starr was born in Liverpool, England. His real name is Richard Starkey.

- My date is divisible by 2, 5, and 10.
- Both my hundreds and tens digits are square numbers, but one is odd and the other is even.

What year am I?

July 8

On July 8 of this year, musician and singer Billy Eckstine was born in Pittsburgh, Pennsylvania. Among Eckstine's hits were "Fools Rush In," "I Apologize," "Blue Moon," and "Body and Soul."

- The two-digit number formed by my thousands and hundreds digits is the eighth prime number.
- The two-digit number formed by my tens and units digits is a multiple of 2 and 7.
- The sum of all of my digits is 15.

What year am I?

On July 8 of this year, German inventor Count Ferdinand von Zeppelin was born. The zeppelin is an airship like the Goodyear blimp.

- My hundreds and units digits are the same cubic number.
- My tens digit is the smallest odd prime number.
- The sum of all of my digits is 20.

What year am I?

July 9

On July 9 of this year, sewing machine inventor Elias Howe was born in Spencer, Massachusetts.

- The two-digit numbers formed by my thousands and hundreds digits and my tens and units digits are consecutive integers; their sum is 37 and their product is 342.
- The two-digit number formed by my tens and units digits is the eighth prime number.

What year am I?

On July 9 of this year, the 14th Amendment to the U.S. Constitution was ratified. It provides due process and equal protection under the law to every citizen.

- The three-digit number formed by my hundreds, tens, and units digits is a palindrome with a sum of 22.
- My hundreds digit is equal to $\sqrt{64}$.

What year am I?

July 10

On July 10 of this year, Mary McLeod Bethune was born in South Carolina. She was the first in her family to be born free. A teacher, she advised President Franklin Roosevelt on minority affairs.

- My date is divisible by 3 and 5.
- My tens and units digits are consecutive primes (in reverse) whose sum is 12 and product is 35.
- My hundreds digit could be the volume of a cube with a side of 2.

What year am I?

On July 10 of this year, black tennis player Arthur Ashe was born in Richmond, Virginia. He won more than 30 titles during his tennis career and was a social activist, known for his work to eliminate racism in America. After contracting the AIDS virus from a blood transfusion, he raised millions of dollars to find a cure for AIDS.

- My units digit raised to the second power is equal to my thousands digit.
- The sum of my units digit and thousands digit is equal to my tens digit.
- The sum of all of my digits is 17.

What year am I?

July 11

On July 11 of this year, a baby boy named Matej Gasper was pronounced the 5-billionth inhabitant of the earth. July 11 is the "Day of the 5 Billion." By the year 2000, the population is expected to exceed 6 billion.

- My hundreds, tens, and units digits are consecutive integers (in reverse order) whose sum is 24.
- My units digit is prime, my tens digit is cubic, and my hundreds digit is square.

What year am I?

On July 11 of this year, the Triborough Bridge in New York City was opened to traffic. The bridge links Manhattan, the Bronx, and Queens.

- The two-digit number formed by my tens and units digits is a multiple of my hundreds digit.
- My tens digit is 50% of my units digit and $33\frac{1}{3}$ % of my hundreds digit.
- The sum of all of my digits is 19.

What year am I?

July 12

On July 12 of this year, American architect Buckminster Fuller was born. He is noted for his design of the geodesic dome.

- My date is divisible by 3 and 5.
- The sum of my thousands and hundreds digits is equal to my tens digit.
- Twice my units digit is equal to the sum of my tens digit and 1.
- The sum of all of my digits is 23.

What year am I?

On July 12 of this year, American author and philosopher Henry Thoreau was born in Concord, Massachusetts. Thoreau loved nature and lived at Walden Pond in Massachusetts.

- The two-digit numbers formed by my thousands and hundreds digits and my tens and units digits are consecutive integers (reversed); their sum is 35.
- The two-digit number formed by my tens and units digits is the seventh prime number.
- The positive difference of my thousands digit and my hundreds digit is equal to my units digit.

What year am I?

July 13

On July 13 of this year, Mary Woolley was born in South Norwalk, Connecticut. She was the first woman to attend classes and graduate from Brown University. She went on to become president of Mt. Holyoke College. Later in her career, she became the first American woman representative at a major diplomatic conference.

- My odd units digit is $\frac{1}{2}$ of my even tens digit.
- My hundreds and tens digits are consecutive even integers (in reverse order) whose sum is 14 and product is 48.
- Because the sum of all of my digits is 18, my date is divisible by 3 and 9.

What year am I?

On July 13 of this year, actor Harrison Ford was born in Chicago, Illinois. Some of the movies he starred in were *Star Wars*, the *Indiana Jones* series, and *Witness*.

- My units digit raised to the second power is equal to my tens digit.
- One more than twice my tens digit is equal to my hundreds digit.
- The sum of all of my digits is 16.

What year am I?

July 14

On July 14 of this year, Jewish-American novelist Isaac Bashevis Singer was born in Poland. The son of a rabbi, Singer was a storyteller who sometimes used imps to narrate his stories.

- My date is divisible by 2 and 4.
- Twice my units digit plus one is equal to my hundreds digit.
- The sum of all of my digits is 14.

What year am I?

On July 14 of this year, Gerald Ford was born in Omaha, Nebraska. The 38th president of the United States, he acquired the office without being elected.

- The two-digit numbers formed by my thousands and hundreds digits and my tens and units digits are prime numbers that are > 10 and < 20.
- If 6 were added to the two-digit number formed by my tens and units digits, it would equal the two-digit number formed by my thousands and hundreds digits.
- The sum of all of my digits is 14.

What year am I?

July 15

On July 15 of this year, Clement Clarke Moore was born in New York City. He was the teacher who wrote "'Twas the Night Before Christmas." The poem was originally called "A Visit from Saint Nicholas."

- My hundreds and tens digits could be the sides of a square with an area of 49.
- My tens and units digits are consecutive odd integers with a sum of 16.
- The sum of all of my digits is 24.

What year am I?

On July 15 of this year, Saint Frances Xavier Cabrini was born. She was the first American saint. The youngest of 13 children, she founded schools, hospitals, and orphanages.

- My date is divisible by 2, 5, and 10.
- My tens digit could be the side of a square with an area of 25.
- My units digit is the additive identity.
- The sum of all of my digits is 14.

What year am I?

July 16

On July 16 of this year, an earthquake registering 7.7 on the Richter scale struck the Philippines. More than 1,600 people were killed and another 1,000 are still missing.

- If my units digit were one greater, my date would be a palindrome with a sum of 20.
- My hundreds and tens digits could be the sides of a square with a perimeter of 36.

What year am I?

On July 16 of this year, African American journalist Ida B. Wells was born in Holly Springs, Mississippi. The daughter of slaves, she traveled the country founding anti-lynching societies and black women's clubs.

- My hundreds, tens, and units digits are all even numbers.
- My units digit is $33\frac{1}{3}\%$ of my tens digit.
- My tens digit is 75% of my hundreds digit.
- The sum of all of my digits is 17.

What year am I?

July 17

On July 17 of this year, author Erle Stanley Gardner was born in Malden, Massachusetts. He is best known for the Perry Mason novels.

- My tens and units digits are consecutive integers with a sum of 17 and a product of 72.
- The difference between my units digit and thousands digit is equal to my hundreds digit.
- The sum of all of my digits is 26.

What year am I?

On July 17 of this year, Douglas Corrigan flew out of Brooklyn, New York, and headed for Los Angeles, California. Twenty-eight hours later, he landed in Dublin, Ireland. When he arrived back in the United States, he was nicknamed "Wrong Way" Corrigan because he had followed the wrong end of the compass needle.

- My date is divisible by 2, 3, and 6.
- My tens digit is $\frac{1}{3}$ of my hundreds digit.
- The sum of my thousands and units digits is equal to my hundreds digit.
- The sum of all of my digits is 21.

What year am I?

July 18

On July 18 of this year, astronaut and Senator John Glenn was born in Cambridge, Ohio. He was the first astronaut to orbit the earth, and was later elected to the U.S. Senate from the state of Ohio.

- The two-digit number formed by my tens and units digits is a multiple of both 7 and 3.
- If my tens digit were 7 greater, my date would be a palindrome with a sum of 20.

What year am I?

On July 18 of this year, Nelson Mandela was born the son of a tribal chieftain in South Africa. He was imprisoned for 28 years for his struggles against apartheid. After his release, he was elected president of South Africa.

- The two-digit numbers formed by my thousands and hundreds digits and by my tens and units digits are consecutive integers in reverse order; their sum is 19.
- My hundreds digit is a square number; my units digit is a cubic number.

What year am I?

July 19

On July 19 of this year, French Impressionist painter Edgar Degas was born in Paris, France. Degas is noted for his paintings of ballerinas.

- My tens and units digits are consecutive integers with a sum of 7.
- My date is even.
- My hundreds digit is 200% of my units digit.

   What year am I?

On July 19 of this year, Nobel-Prize-winning medical physicist Rosalyn Yalow was born in New York City. Her study of the applications of radioactive isotopes led to studies of insulin and diabetes.

- The two-digit numbers formed by my thousands and hundreds digits and my tens and units digits are consecutive odd integers with a sum of 40.
- If my hundreds digit were seven less, my date would be a palindrome.

   What year am I?

July 20

On July 20 of this year, explorer and mountaineer Sir Edmund Percival Hillary was born in New Zealand. With his Sherpa guide, Tenzing Norgay, he became the first person to climb Mount Everest.

- The two-digit number formed by my thousands and hundreds digits is the eighth prime number.
- If my tens and units digits were reversed, my date would be a palindrome.
- The sum of all of my digits is 20.

   What year am I?

On July 20 of this year, astronaut Neil Armstrong became the first person to land on the moon. When he stepped on the moon, he said: "That's one small step for a man, one giant leap for mankind."

- My tens digit is a perfect number.
- My hundreds and units digits are the same square number.
- The sum of all of my digits is 25.

   What year am I?

July 21

On July 21 of this year, novelist Ernest Hemingway was born in Oak Park, Illinois. The American Nobel Prize winner wrote *The Sun Also Rises, For Whom the Bell Tolls,* and *The Old Man and the Sea.*

- My hundreds and tens digits are consecutive integers with a sum of 17 and a product of 72.
- My tens and units digits could be the side of a square with a perimeter of 36 and an area of 81.
- The sum of my thousands and hundreds digits is equal to my tens digit.

What year am I?

On July 21 of this year, violinist Isaac Stern was born.

- My date is divisible by 2, 3, 4, 5, 6, and 10.
- The two-digit number formed by my tens and units digits is one greater than the two-digit number formed by my thousands and hundreds digits.
- The sum of all of my digits is 12.

What year am I?

July 22

On July 22 of this year, Austrian biologist Gregor Mendel was born. He experimented with plants and developed theories related to heredity and genetics.

- My tens and units digits are the same even prime number.
- The sum of my tens and units digits is $\frac{1}{2}$ of my hundreds digit.
- The sum of all of my digits is 13.

What year am I?

On July 22 of this year, American poet Emma Lazarus was born. Words from her poem "The New Colossus" appear at the base of the Statue of Liberty. They are "Give me your tired, your poor, your huddled masses yearning to breathe free."

- The square root of the two-digit number formed by my tens and units digits is 7.
- My hundreds digit is 200% of my tens digit.
- The sum of my thousands and hundreds digits is equal to my units digit.
- The sum of all of my digits is 22.

What year am I?

July 23

On July 23 of this year, Albert Warner was born. He was the Polish American who founded Warner Brothers Productions.

- My hundreds and tens digits are the same cubic number.
- My units digit is 50% of my tens digit.
- My date is divisible by 2, 3, and 6.

   What year am I?

On July 23 of this year, baseball player and broadcast announcer Don Drysdale was born in Van Nuys, California. He was elected to the Baseball Hall of Fame after compiling a win-loss record of 209–166 and a lifetime earned-run average of 2.95.

- The two-digit number formed by my tens and units digits is a multiple of my hundreds digit.
- My tens digit is $\frac{1}{3}$ of my hundreds digit but $\frac{1}{2}$ of my units digit.
- The sum of all of my digits is 19.

   What year am I?

July 24

On July 24 of this year, aviator Amelia Earhart was born in Atchison, Kansas. The first woman to cross the Atlantic, she was lost on a flight from New Guinea to Howland Island in the Pacific Ocean.

- The three-digit number formed by my hundreds, tens, and units digits is a palindrome with a sum of 25.
- My hundreds and units digits are even; my tens digit is odd.

   What year am I?

On July 24 of this year, French novelist Alexandre Dumas was born. He wrote *The Count of Monte Cristo* and *The Three Musketeers*.

- My units digit is $\frac{1}{4}$ of my hundreds digit.
- My tens digit is the additive identity.
- The sum of all of my digits is 11.

   What year am I?

July 25

On July 25 of this year, Walter Payton was born in Columbia, Mississippi. The Pro Football Hall of Famer played for the Chicago Bears.

- The sum of my tens and units digits is equal to my hundreds digit.
- My even units digit is one less than my prime tens digit.
- The sum of my thousands and hundreds digits is twice my tens digit.

What year am I?

On July 25 of this year, the first carousel was patented.

- If my tens digits were one greater, my date would be a palindrome.
- My hundreds digit is a cubic number; my tens digit is a prime number.
- The sum of all of my digits is 17.

What year am I?

July 26

On July 26 of this year, Irish dramatist and Nobel Prize winner George Bernard Shaw was born. Among his many plays was *Pygmalion,* which inspired the musical *My Fair Lady.*

- My tens and units digits are consecutive integers with a sum of 11 and a product of 30.
- My perfect units digit is $\frac{3}{4}$ of my hundreds digit.
- The sum of my thousands and tens digits is equal to my units digit.

What year am I?

On July 26 of this year, singer and musician Mick Jagger was born in Dartford, England. He is the lead singer for the Rolling Stones; among the songs he has written are "Satisfaction," "Ruby Tuesday," and "Honky-Tonk Woman."

- My units digit is $\frac{1}{3}$ of my hundreds digit.
- Both my hundreds and tens digits are square numbers, but one is odd and the other is even.
- The sum of all of my digits is 17.

What year am I?

   730 Daily Math Warm-ups

July 27

On July 27 of this year, the armistice agreement that ended the Korean War was signed in Panmunjom, Korea. (It was signed on July 26 U.S. time.) The war lasted just over 3 years, but the armistice talks took 2 years 17 days.

- My tens and units digits are prime numbers, but my units digit is two less than my tens digit.
- My hundreds digit is three times larger than my units digit.
- My date is divisible by 3 and 9.

What year am I?

On July 27 of this year, Congress established the first national department whose job it was to deal with foreign affairs. Originally called the Department of Foreign Affairs, it is now the Department of State.

- My hundreds, tens, and units digits are consecutive integers whose sum is 24.

What year am I?

July 28

On July 28 of this year, Jacqueline Kennedy Onassis was born in Southampton, New York. An editor and the wife of John Fitzgerald Kennedy, she later married Greek shipping tycoon Aristotle Onassis.

- The three-digit number formed by my hundreds, tens, and units digits is a palindrome with a sum of 20.
- My thousands digit plus four times my tens digit is equal to my units digit.

What year am I?

On July 28 of this year, Terry Fox was born. He was the Canadian youth responsible for the "Marathon of Hope." When Terry needed to have his right leg amputated because of cancer, he planned a 5,200-mile run across Canada using an artificial leg. He raised $24 million for cancer research before he had to discontinue his quest after running 3,328 miles. He died one month short of his 24th birthday.

- The sum of my thousands and hundreds digits is two times my tens digit.
- My units digit is equal to $\sqrt{64}$.
- The sum of all of my digits is 23.

What year am I?

July 29

On July 29 of this year, inventor Charles William Beebe was born. In his invention, the bathysphere, he was able to go over 3,000 feet below sea level to explore the seas.

- My tens and units digits could be the sides of a square with a perimeter of 28.
- My hundreds digit minus my thousands digit is equal to my tens digit.

What year am I?

On July 29 of this year, the American ship *Indianapolis* was torpedoed by a submarine. Of the 1,196 crew members aboard, only 318 survived. This is the U.S. Navy's worst loss at sea.

- The sum of my tens and units digits is equal to my hundreds digit.
- My tens and units digits are consecutive integers whose product is 20.
- The sum of all of my digits is 19.

What year am I?

July 30

On July 30 of this year, automobile inventor Henry Ford was born. He once said, "Failure is only the opportunity to more intelligently begin again."

- The sum of my tens and units digits is equal to the sum of my thousands and hundreds digits.
- My units digit is 50% of my tens digit; my tens digit is 75% of my hundreds digit.
- The sum of all of my digits is 18.

What year am I?

On July 30 of this year, English novelist Emily Brontë was born. Her best known novel is *Wuthering Heights*.

- The two-digit number formed by my thousands and hundreds digits is the same number as the two-digit number formed by my tens and units digits.
- My date is divisible by 2, 3, 6, and 9.
- The sum of all of my digits is 18.

What year am I?

July 31

On July 31 of this year, President Harry Truman dedicated the International Airport at New York City as 900 airplanes flew overhead. Originally called Idlewild Field, it was later renamed Kennedy International Airport.

- Both my tens and units digits are even numbers; my tens digit is $\frac{1}{2}$ of my units digit.
- The sum of my thousands and hundreds digits is two less than the sum of my tens and units digits.
- The sum of all of my digits is 22.

What year am I?

On July 31 of this year, the cornerstone of the first U.S. government building was positioned in Philadelphia. It was the U.S. Mint.

- My units digit raised to the third power is equal to the sum of my thousands and hundreds digits.
- The two-digit number formed by my hundreds and tens digits is the 22nd prime number.
- The sum of all of my digits is 19.

What year am I?

August 1

On August 1 of this year, astronomer Maria Mitchell was born in Nantucket, Massachusetts. Her abilities in mathematics led to her career as the first professional astronomer, in which she won many honors.

- The two-digit number formed by my tens and units digits is the same as the two-digit number formed by my thousands and hundreds digits.
- The sum of all of my digits is 18.

What year am I?

On August 1 of this year, Anne Frank wrote her final entry in her journal. Three days after writing "I keep on trying to find a way of becoming what I would like to be, and what I could be if . . . there weren't any other people living in the world," the young girl hiding from the Nazis was found and sent to Bergen-Belsen concentration camp.

- My date is divisible by 2, 3, 4, 6, and 9.
- My tens and units digits could be the sides of a square with both a perimeter and an area of 16.

What year am I?

August 2

On August 2 of this year, African American author James Baldwin was born in New York City. His best known work is *Go Tell It on the Mountain*.

- The two-digit number formed by my tens and units digits is equal to 4!.
- My units digit is twice my tens digit.
- The sum of all of my digits is 16.

What year am I?

On August 2 of this year, architect and engineer Pierre-Charles L'Enfant was born in Paris, France. L'Enfant, an officer in the Revolutionary War, designed the plan for the city of Washington, D.C.

- Both my hundreds and tens digits are prime numbers, but my tens digit is two less than my hundreds digit.
- My units digit is $\frac{1}{2}$ the sum of my thousands and hundreds digits.
- The sum of all of my digits is 17.

What year am I?

August 3

On August 3 of this year, Elisha Graves Otis was born. He was the inventor and manufacturer of the elevator.

- The two-digit number formed by my tens and units digits is the smallest two-digit prime number.
- The prime factors of the two-digit number formed by my thousands and hundreds digits are 2×3^2.

What year am I?

On August 3 of this year, singer Tony Bennett (Anthony Dominick Benedetto) was born in New York City.

- My date is divisible by 2, 3, 6, and 9.
- My units digit is $\frac{2}{3}$ of my hundreds digit.
- My tens digit is $\frac{1}{3}$ of my units digit.

What year am I?

August 4

On August 4 of this year, three civil rights workers were found murdered. The deaths of James Chaney, Andrew Goodman, and Michael Schwerner inspired the movie *Mississippi Burning*.

- My tens digit is $\frac{2}{3}$ of my hundreds digit; my units digit is $\frac{2}{3}$ of my tens digit.
- The sum of my thousands and hundreds digits is equal to the sum of my tens and units digits.
- The prime factors of the two-digit number formed by my tens and units digits is 2^6.

What year am I?

On August 4 of this year, Raoul Wallenberg was born in Stockholm, Sweden. Wallenberg was granted honorary American citizenship for saving 100,000 Jews from the Nazis.

- The sum of my tens and units digits is $\frac{1}{3}$ of my hundreds digit.
- The three-digit number formed by my thousands, hundreds, and tens digits is a palindrome with a sum of 11.
- My date is divisible by 2.

What year am I?

August 5

On August 5 of this year, the first English colony in North America was founded on the island of Newfoundland. Sir Humphrey Gilbert established the colony in the area around Saint John's Harbor.

- Both my hundreds and units digits are prime numbers; my units digit is two less than my hundreds digit.
- The sum of my hundreds and units digits is equal to my tens digit.
- My tens digit is equal to 2^3.
- The sum of all of my digits is 17.

What year am I?

On August 5 of this year, astronaut Neil Alden Armstrong was born in Wapakoneta, Ohio. He was the first person to walk on the moon.

- My tens digit is $\frac{1}{3}$ of my hundreds digit.
- My units digit is the additive identity element.
- The sum of all of my digits is 13.

What year am I?

August 6

On August 6 of this year, comedienne Lucille Ball was born in Butte, Montana. The star of many TV shows and movies, she will always be remembered for the TV sitcom *I Love Lucy*.

- The two-digit prime number formed by my tens and units digits is two more than my hundreds digit.
- The sum of all of my digits is 12.

What year am I?

On August 6 of this year, President Lyndon Johnson signed the Voting Rights Act into law. The act is meant to prevent discrimination against minorities in election practices.

- The two-digit number formed by my tens and units digits is divisible by 5 and 13.
- My tens digit is $\frac{2}{3}$ of my hundreds digit.
- The sum of all of my digits is 21.

What year am I?

August 7

On August 7 of this year, American statesman and Nobel Peace Prize winner Ralph Johnson Bunche was born in Detroit, Michigan.

- Both my hundreds and units digits are square numbers, but one is odd and the other is even.
- My date is divisible by 2 and 4.
- The sum of all of my digits is 14.

What year am I?

On August 7 of this year, the first picture of the earth was received from the space satellite *Explorer VI*. It was the first time the people of Earth could see their planet.

- My hundreds, tens, and units digits form a palindrome with a sum of 23.
- The two-digit number formed by my tens and units digits is the 17th prime number.

What year am I?

August 8

On August 8 of this year, Odie first appeared in the "Garfield" cat comic strip as Garfield's sidekick.

- My tens and units digits are consecutive integers with a sum of 15 and a product of 56.
- My date is divisible by 2.
- The sum of all of my digits is 25.

What year am I?

On August 8 of this year, actor Dustin Hoffman was born in Los Angeles, California. He starred in *Rain Man, Kramer vs. Kramer, The Graduate,* and *Midnight Cowboy.*

- My tens digit is $\frac{1}{3}$ of my hundreds digit.
- The sum of my thousands and hundreds digits is equal to the sum of my tens and units digits.
- My units digit is the largest single-digit prime number.

What year am I?

August 9

On August 9 of this year, the resignation of Richard Milhous Nixon from the presidency of the United States became effective at noon. Under threat of impeachment because of the Watergate scandal, Nixon became the first to resign the presidency.

- My date is divisible by 2, 3, and 6.
- The two-digit number formed by my hundreds and tens digits is the largest prime number < 100.
- My tens digit is the largest prime number < 10.

What year am I?

On August 9 of this year, African American track star Jesse Owens became the first person to win four gold medals in the Olympic Games.

- The two-digit number formed by my tens and units digits is a multiple of my hundreds digit.
- My tens digit is $\frac{1}{3}$ of my hundreds digit and $\frac{1}{2}$ of my units digit.
- The sum of all of my digits is 19.

What year am I?

August 10

On August 10 of this year, Missouri became the 24th state admitted to the United States.

- The two-digit number formed by my tens and units digits is a multiple of 3.
- My tens digit raised to the third power is equal to my hundreds digit.
- The sum of all of my digits is 12.

What year am I?

On August 10 of this year, the Smithsonian Institution in Washington, D.C., was founded.

- My tens digit is 50% of my hundreds digit and $\frac{2}{3}$ of my units digit.
- My tens and units digits are consecutive even integers with a sum of 10 and a product of 24.

What year am I?

August 11

On August 11 of this year, orator Frederick Douglass first spoke before an audience. He spoke at an antislavery convention about his life as a slave. Douglass was so eloquent that he became a full-time lecturer for the Anti-Slavery Society.

- My tens digit is 50% of my hundreds digit.
- If my tens digit were four greater, my date would be a palindrome.
- The sum of all of my digits is 14.

What year am I?

On August 11 of this year, *Roots* author Alex Palmer Haley was born in Ithaca, New York.

- The two-digit number formed by my tens and units digits is a multiple of 3 and 7.
- The sum of my tens and units digits is $\frac{1}{3}$ of my hundreds digit.

What year am I?

August 12

On August 12 of this year, comic actor Cantinflas was born in Mexico City. His real name is Mario Moreno Reyes. Mexico's most famous comic actor, he is known internationally for his role in *Around the World in 80 Days*.

- My hundreds digit and the two-digit number formed by my tens and units digits are consecutive odd integers whose sum is 20 and whose product is 99.
- The two-digit number formed by my tens and units digits is the smallest prime number greater than 10.

What year am I?

On August 12 of this year, American Baseball Hall of Famer Christy Mathewson was born in Factoryville, Pennsylvania. In 17 years, he won 372 games, lost 188, and struck out 2,499 batters.

- My date is divisible by 2, 5, and 10.
- My hundreds and tens digits could be the sides of a square with a perimeter of 32.
- The sum of all of my digits is 17.

What year am I?

August 13

On August 13 of this year, the East German government closed the border between East and West Berlin with barbed-wire fences. Telephone service and mail were interrupted. Later in the week, a concrete wall was built which separated East and West for over 25 years.

- My tens digit is $\frac{2}{3}$ of my hundreds digit.
- My units digit is the multiplicative identity element.
- The sum of all of my digits is 17.

What year am I?

On August 13 of this year, English film director Alfred Hitchcock was born. The master of suspense directed his well-known TV series, *The Alfred Hitchcock Show*, and many movies, including *Rear Window, The Birds, Psycho,* and *Frenzy*.

- The two-digit number formed by my tens and units digits is the largest number < 100.
- The sum of my thousands and hundreds digits is equal to my tens digit.

What year am I?

August 14

On August 14 of this year, Ernest Lawrence Thayer was born in Lawrence, Massachusetts. The author of "Casey at the Bat," he was paid $5 when the poem was first published in the *San Francisco Examiner*.

- My units digit is $\frac{1}{2}$ of my tens digit; my tens digit is $\frac{3}{4}$ of my hundreds digit.
- My date is divisible by 3 and 9 but not by 2.
- The sum of my thousands and hundreds digits is equal to the sum of my tens and units digits.

What year am I?

On August 14 of this year, Congress approved the Social Security Act. This act pays benefits to older Americans and their survivors.

- My date is divisible by 3, 5, and 9.
- My hundreds digit is three times the size of my tens digit.
- The positive difference between my thousands and hundreds digits is equal to the sum of my tens and units digits.

What year am I?

August 15

On August 15 of this year, the French emperor Napoleon Bonaparte was born on the island of Corsica.

- The two-digit number formed by my thousands and hundreds digits is the seventh prime number.
- My tens digit is $\frac{2}{3}$ of my units digit; my units digit is $1\frac{1}{2}$ times my tens digit.
- The sum of all of my digits is 23.

What year am I?

On August 15 of this year, Edna Ferber was born in Kalamazoo, Michigan. The Pulitzer Prize winner wrote many novels, including the commercial success *So Big*.

- The two-digit number formed by my tens and units digits is a multiple of 3 and 29.
- My hundreds and tens digits could be the sides of a square with an area of 64 and a perimeter of 32.

What year am I?

August 16

On August 16 of this year, Menachem Begin was born in Poland. A fighter for Israeli independence, he became prime minister of Israel and signed a peace treaty with Egypt at Camp David.

- The two-digit numbers formed by my tens and units digits and my thousands and hundreds digits are both prime numbers; one is six greater than the other.
- My units digit is $\frac{1}{3}$ the size of my hundreds digit.
- The sum of all of my digits is 14.

What year am I?

On August 16 of this year, singer Elvis Presley died at the Memphis Baptist Hospital. He was one of America's most popular singers.

- My tens and units digits could be the sides of a square with a perimeter of 28 and an area of 49.
- The two-digit number formed by my hundreds and tens digits is the largest prime number < 100.

What year am I?

August 17

On August 17 of this year, three Americans—Max Anderson, Ben Abruzzo, and Larry Newman—became the first to cross the Atlantic in a hot-air balloon. They traveled 3,200 miles in a little over 137 hours.

- My hundreds, tens, and units digits are consecutive integers completely out of order; their mean is 8.
- My hundreds digit is a square number; my tens digit is prime; my units digit is cubic.

What year am I?

On August 17 of this year, American frontiersman Davy Crockett was born in Hawkins County, Tennessee. He died defending the Alamo.

- My date is divisible by 2, 3, and 6.
- My units digit is 75% of my tens digit.
- The sum of my thousands and hundreds digits is equal to my tens digit.

What year am I?

August 18

On August 18 of this year, Virginia Dare was born on Roanoke Island, North Carolina. She was the first child of English parents born in the New World.

- The prime factors of the two-digit number formed by my tens and units digits are 29 and 3.
- My hundreds digit is the third prime number.
- The sum of all of my digits is 21.

What year am I?

On August 18 of this year, actor and director Robert Redford was born in Santa Monica, California. Redford starred in *Butch Cassidy and the Sundance Kid* and directed *A River Runs Through It*.

- My tens digit is $\frac{1}{3}$ of my hundreds digit.
- The sum of my thousands and hundreds digits is equal to the sum of my tens and units digits.
- The sum of all of my digits is 20.

What year am I?

August 19

On August 19 of this year, American writer Ogden Nash was born in Rye, New York. He is known for humorous verse, such as:

> The ant has made himself illustrious
> Through constant industry industrious. So what?
> Would you be calm and placid
> If you were full of formic acid?

- My date is divisible by 2, 3, and 6.
- My units digit is the only even prime number.
- My hundreds digit is equal to $\sqrt{81}$.
- The sum of all of my digits is 12.

What year am I?

On August 19 of this year, Gene Roddenberry was born in El Paso, Texas. He was the creator of the TV series *Star Trek*.

- The two-digit numbers formed by my thousands and hundreds digits and my tens and units digits are consecutive odd integers.
- The sum of my tens and units digits is $\frac{1}{3}$ of my hundreds digit.
- If my tens digits were seven greater, my date would be a palindrome.

What year am I?

August 20

On August 20 of this year, Benjamin Harrison was born in North Bend, Ohio. The 23rd president of the United States, he was the nephew of William Harrison, our ninth president.

- My tens and units digits could be the sides of a square with an area of 9 and a perimeter of 12.
- The sum of my thousands and hundreds digits is equal to the product of my tens and units digits.

What year am I?

On August 20 of this year, American author H.P. Lovecraft was born in Providence, Rhode Island. He wrote tales of horror and the supernatural.

- My date is divisible by 2, 3, 5, 6, 9, and 10.
- My hundreds and tens digits are consecutive integers with a sum of 17 and a product of 72.
- The sum of my thousands and hundreds digits is equal to my tens digit.

What year am I?

August 21

On August 21 of this year, Hawaii became the 50th state of the United States. The proclamation was signed by President Dwight Eisenhower.

- The three-digit number formed by my hundreds, tens, and units digits is a palindrome with a sum of 23.
- My tens digit is the third prime number.
- If my hundreds and units digits were the sides of a cube, its area would be 81 and its perimeter would be 36.

What year am I?

On August 21 of this year, Basketball Hall of Famer Wilt Chamberlain was born in Philadelphia, Pennsylvania.

- The two-digit number formed by my tens and units digits is a multiple of my hundreds digit.
- My tens digit is $\frac{1}{2}$ of my units digit and $\frac{1}{3}$ of my hundreds digit.
- The sum of all of my digits is 19.

What year am I?

August 22

On August 22 of this year, American author Ray Bradbury was born in Waukegan, Illinois. He wrote *Fahrenheit 451*. (Did you know that paper burns at a temperature of 451° Fahrenheit?)

- My date is divisible by 2, 3, 5, 6, and 10.
- The prime factors of the two-digit number formed by my tens and units digits is $2^2 \times 5$.
- The sum of all of my digits is 12.

What year am I?

On August 22 of this year, French musician and composer Claude Debussy was born. One of his well-known pieces is "Clair de Lune."

- My units digit is $\frac{1}{4}$ of my hundreds digit and $\frac{1}{3}$ of my tens digit.
- My tens digit is equal to $3!$.
- My hundreds digit is equal to 2^3.

What year am I?

August 23

On August 23 of this year, American naval hero Commodore Oliver Perry died in Trinidad, West Indies. He is best known for his announcement of victory at the Battle of Lake Erie: "We have met the enemy, and they are ours."

- The two-digit numbers formed by my thousands and hundreds digits and my tens and units digits are consecutive integers with a sum of 37.
- My hundreds digit is equal to 2^3; my units digit is equal to 3^2.

What year am I?

On August 23 of this year, actor and dancer Gene Kelly was born in Pittsburgh, Pennsylvania. Two of the movies he starred in were *An American in Paris* and *Singin' in the Rain*.

- The prime factorization of the two-digit number formed by my tens and units digits is $2^2 \times 3$.
- The sum of my tens and units digits is equal to $\frac{1}{3}$ of my hundreds digit.
- The sum of all of my digits is 13.

What year am I?

August 24

On August 24 of this year, the volcano Vesuvius erupted, destroying the cities of Pompeii, Stabiae, and Herculaneum in southern Italy.

- My date is the largest prime number < 80.
- My tens digit and units digit are consecutive odd integers.
- The sum of all of my digits (as few as they are) is 16.

What year am I?

On August 24 of this year, British forces invaded Washington, D.C., burning the Capitol, the president's house, and many other public buildings. President James Madison fled to safety until the British left two days later.

- My units digit is 50% of my hundreds digit.
- My hundreds digit is equal to 2^3; my units digit is equal to 2^2.
- The sum of all of my digits is 14.

What year am I?

August 25

On August 25 of this year, American cartoonist Walt Kelly was born in Philadelphia, Pennsylvania. He created the comic strip "Pogo."

- The two-digit number formed by my tens and units digits is the sixth prime number; the two-digit number formed by my thousands and hundreds digits is the eighth prime number.
- The sum of all of my digits is 14.

What year am I?

On August 25 of this year, American writer Bret Harte was born in Albany, New York. He is best remembered for his western stories, including "The Outcasts of Poker Flat," "The Luck of Roaring Camp," and "How Santa Claus Came to Simpson's Bar."

- The sum of my thousands and hundreds digits is equal to the sum of my tens and units digits.
- My units digit is 200% of my tens digit.
- My units digit is 75% of my hundreds digit.
- My date is divisible by 2, 3, 4, 6, and 9.

What year am I?

August 26

On August 26 of this year, French chemist Antoine Lavoisier was born. He discovered the element oxygen, working independently of Joseph Priestley, the codiscoverer of oxygen.

- The two-digit number formed by my tens and units digits is the 14th prime number.
- The sum of my tens and units digits is equal to my hundreds digit.
- My hundreds digit is the largest single-digit prime number.
- The sum of all of my digits is 15.

What year am I?

On August 26 of this year, the 19th Amendment to the U.S. Constitution was ratified. It gave women the right to vote.

- My date is divisible by 2, 3, 4, 5, 6, and 10.
- One more than four times my tens digit is equal to my hundreds digit.
- The sum of all of my digits is 12.

What year am I?

August 27

On August 27 of this year, the ancient Chinese philosopher Confucius is believed to have been born. The date is so far in the past that nobody knows for sure.

- The sum of my three-digit date is 11.
- My hundreds and tens digits could be the sides of a square with an area of 25 and a perimeter of 20.

What year am I?

On August 27 of this year, Lyndon Baines Johnson was born near Stonewall, Texas. The 36th president of the United States, he succeeded to the presidency following the assassination of John F. Kennedy.

- My date is divisible by 2, 3, 4, 6, and 9.
- My units digit is equal to the square root of 64.
- The sum of all of my digits is 18.

What year am I?

August 28

On August 28 of this year, New York radio station WEAF ran an advertisement for a realtor. It was the first time an ad was broadcast; ten minutes of airtime cost $100.

- The two-digit number formed by my tens and units digits is a multiple of 2 and 11.
- My hundreds digit is equal to $\sqrt{81}$.
- The sum of all of my digits is 14.

What year am I?

On August 28 of this year, Delaware Bay was discovered by Henry Hudson.

- My hundreds digit is $\frac{2}{3}$ of my units digit.
- My tens digit is the additive identity element.
- The sum of all of my digits is 16.

What year am I?

August 29

On August 29 of this year, legendary jazz saxophonist Charlie Parker was born in Kansas City, Kansas. He earned the nickname "Yardbird" (or "Bird") from sitting in his backyard and playing his saxophone.

- My date would be written as 1.92×10^3 in scientific notation.

What year am I?

On August 29 of this year, motion picture actress Ingrid Bergman was born in Sweden. She won three Oscars and starred in the famous movie *Casablanca*.

- The two-digit number formed by my tens and units digits is a multiple of 3 and 5.
- The two-digit number formed by my thousands and hundreds digits is the largest prime number < 20.

What year am I?

August 30

On August 30 of this year, Ester Cleveland became the first baby to be born to the wife of a president in the White House.

- My units digit is $\frac{1}{3}$ of my tens digit.
- The sum of my thousands and hundreds digits is equal to my tens digit.
- The sum of all of my digits is 21.

What year am I?

On August 30 of this year, actor Fred MacMurray was born in Kankakee, Illinois. He starred in comedies, including *The Absent Minded Professor, Son of Flubber, The Shaggy Dog,* and *The Happiest Millionaire,* and in the TV series *My Three Sons.*

- My hundreds digit is a square number; my units digit is a cubic number.
- My tens digit is the additive identity.
- The sum of all of my digits is 18.

What year am I?

August 31

On August 31 of this year, the first major earthquake recorded in the United States occurred in Charleston, South Carolina. The quake was felt up to 800 miles away; it is believed that about 100 people died.

- My hundreds and tens digits could be the sides of a square with a perimeter of 32 and an area of 64.
- My even units digit is $\frac{3}{4}$ of my hundreds digit.

What year am I?

On August 31 of this year, Meriwether Lewis and William Clark began their exploration of the western United States.

- My date is divisible by 3.
- My hundreds digit is equal to one less than three times my units digit.
- The sum of all of my digits is 12.

What year am I?

September 1

On September 1 of this year, Korean Airlines Flight 007 was shot down by a Soviet interceptor plane when it reportedly strayed more than 100 miles off course into Soviet airspace. The 269 people on board were killed.

- My tens digit is an even number which is one less than my hundreds digit.
- The product of my tens and units digits is 24; the sum is 11.

What year am I?

On September 1 of this year, Emma M. Nutt began her job as the first woman telephone operator. She worked in Boston, Massachusetts, for the next 33 years.

- My hundreds and units digits are the same even number, 2^3.
- The sum of all of my digits is 24.

What year am I?

September 2

On September 2 of this year, New Hampshire high school teacher Christa McAuliffe was born. She was to be the first "ordinary citizen" to travel in space. She was part of a seven-member crew of the space shuttle *Challenger*, which exploded on January 28, 1986.

- The sum of my tens and units digits is 12; the product is 32.
- The sum of all of my digits is 22.

What year am I?

On September 2 of this year, the Great Fire of London started in the wooden house of a baker named Farryner, near the Tower of London.

- My hundreds, tens, and units digits are the same perfect number.
- The sum of all of my digits is 19.

What year am I?

September 3

On September 3 of this year, Prudence Crandall was born. She was a very brave American schoolteacher who, when her private academy for girls was boycotted because she admitted a black girl, started a school for "young ladies and misses of color."

- The sum of my digits is 12.
- My hundreds digit is the largest single-digit even number.
- My units digit is the first odd prime number.

What year am I?

On September 3 of this year, the Treaty of Paris was signed, ending the Revolutionary War. The signers representing America were John Adams, Benjamin Franklin, and John Jay.

- My hundreds and units digits are prime numbers.
- My tens digit is 2^3.
- The sum of all of my digits is 19.

What year am I?

September 4

On September 4 of this year, American architect Daniel Burnham was born in Henderson, New York. He proposed the long-range plan for Chicago that has kept the city's lakefront one of the most beautiful in the United States.

- My hundreds, tens, and units digits are all even numbers.
- My hundreds digit is larger than my units digit; my tens digit is smaller than my units digit.
- None of my digits are prime numbers.

What year am I?

On September 4 of this year, Barney Flaherty was hired by the *New York Sun* as the first newsboy. He was 10 years old.

- My tens digit and my units digit are the same prime number.
- The sum of my tens and units digits is 6; the product is 9.
- The sum of all of my digits is 15.

What year am I?

September 5

On September 5 of this year, Michigan's Great Fire began. Over a million acres were devastated and at least 125 people died. The newly formed Red Cross furnished disaster relief for the victims and won the support of all Americans for its prompt aid.

- My digits form a palindrome.
- My hundreds and tens digits are the same even number.
- My hundreds and tens digits could be the sides of a square with a perimeter of 24.

What year am I?

On September 5 of this year, comedian Bob Newhart was born in Chicago, Illinois.

- My hundreds and units digits are the same.
- My units digit is an odd square number.
- The sum of all of my digits is 21.

What year am I?

September 6

On September 6 of this year, songwriter Billy Rose was born in New York City. Rose was also a theatrical producer and author. His songs include "That Old Gang of Mine," "Me and My Shadow," and "It's Only a Paper Moon."

- The sum of my thousands digit and hundreds digit equals my tens digit.
- My tens digit and my units digit are the same.

What year am I?

On September 6 of this year, American social reformer Jane Addams was born. She was a great humanitarian and founded Hull House in Chicago, Illinois, to help poor immigrants. Through her efforts, child labor laws to protect young children were enacted.

- My hundreds digit and my tens digit are even numbers whose sum is 14 and product is 48.
- My units digit is the additive identity.
- The sum of all of my digits is 15.

What year am I?

September 7

On September 7 of this year, Queen Elizabeth I of England was born. She was the daughter of Henry VIII and Anne Boleyn.

- My hundreds, tens, and units digits are all prime numbers.
- The two-digit number formed by my tens and units digits is a multiple of 11.
- My hundreds digit and my tens digit are consecutive primes in reverse order.
- The sum of all of my digits is only 12.

What year am I?

On September 7 of this year, American painter Grandma Moses (Anna Mary Moses) was born. She started painting at the age of 78.

- My hundreds digit is 2^3.
- The sum of my tens digit and units digit is 6; their product is 0.
- My units digit is the smallest of all whole numbers.

What year am I?

September 8

On September 8 of this year, the first Miss America was crowned in Atlantic City, New Jersey. She was Margaret Gorman of Washington, D.C.

- My thousands digit and my units digit are the same number.
- The product of my hundreds digit and tens digit is 18; the sum is 11.
- My hundreds digit could be the area of a square.

What year am I?

On September 8 of this year, the first episode of *Star Trek* aired on the NBC television network.

- Both my tens digit and units digit are perfect numbers.
- The sum of all of my digits is 22.

What year am I?

September 9

On September 9 of this year, California became the 31st state.

- My hundreds digit is even.
- My tens digit is $\sqrt{25}$.
- My units digit is the additive identity.

   What year am I?

On September 9 of this year, William the Conqueror fought the Battle of Hastings.

- My tens and units digits are perfect numbers.
- The sum of all of my digits is 13.

   What year am I?

September 10

On September 10 of this year, the American Olympic basketball team lost to the Soviet team when the officials incorrectly placed an extra three seconds on the clock. The Americans refused to accept their silver medals and boycotted the awards ceremony. To this day, they believe they won the gold on that September 10.

- The sum of my tens digit and units digit is equal to my hundreds digit.
- My units digit is an even prime number.
- The sum of all of my digits is 19.

   What year am I?

On September 10 of this year, Declaration of Independence signer Carter Braxton was born in Newington, Virginia.

- Both my hundreds digit and tens digit are prime numbers.
- My units digit is twice my tens digit and one less than my hundreds digit.

   What year am I?

September 11

On September 11 of this year, the entire cabinet of President John Tyler resigned in protest of his veto of the Banking Bill.

- My thousands digit and units digit are the same.
- My tens digit is exactly $\frac{1}{2}$ of my hundreds digit.

What year am I?

On September 11 of this year, American author William Sidney Porter was born in Greensboro, North Carolina. You might be more familiar with Mr. Porter's pen name, O. Henry.

- All of my digits (except for the thousands) are even.
- My units digit is $\sqrt{4}$.
- The sum of my units digit and tens digit is equal to my hundreds digit.

What year am I?

September 12

On September 12 of this year, American athlete Jesse Owens (James Cleveland Owens) was born in Oakville, Alabama. He won four gold medals at the 1936 Olympic Games in Berlin, Germany, and set 11 world records in track and field. At one meet, he broke five world records and tied a sixth—all in the space of 45 minutes.

- My units digit is the square root of my hundreds digit.
- My thousands digit is the same as my tens digit.
- The two-digit number formed by my thousands and hundreds digits is a prime number; it is six more than the two-digit number formed by my tens and units digits.

What year am I?

On September 12 of this year, *Luna 2* landed on the moon. The unmanned Soviet spacecraft was the first spacecraft on the moon.

- My hundreds digit and my units digit are the same.
- The sum of my thousands digit and my tens digit is a perfect number.
- My hundreds, tens, and units digits form a palindrome with a sum of 23.

What year am I?

September 13

On September 13 of this year, the Congress picked New York City as the seat of the new U.S. government.

- My tens digit and my units digit are the same cubic number.
- My hundreds digit is prime.
- The sum of all of my digits is 24.

What year am I?

On September 13 of this year, singer and composer Mel Torme was born in Chicago, Illinois. You probably know him as the favorite singer of the judge on *Night Court*, the TV situation comedy.

- Both my tens digit and my units digit are prime numbers; their GCF is 1, but their LCM is 10.
- My units digit is larger than my tens digit but smaller than my hundreds digit.
- The sum of my thousands and hundreds digits is equal to the product of my tens and units digits.

What year am I?

September 14

On September 14 of this year, 56-year-old balloonist Joe Kittinger left Caribou, Maine, in a balloon named *Rosie O'Grady's Balloon of Peace* to cross the Atlantic. His 84-hour flight covered 3,535 miles and was the first solo crossing of the Atlantic by balloon.

- While my thousands and hundreds digits are odd, my tens and units digits are even.
- My tens digit is twice my units digit.
- If my units digit and tens digit were the sides of a rectangle, the perimeter would be 24.

What year am I?

On September 14 of this year, Italian poet Dante Alighieri died in Ravenna, Italy. He wrote the *Divine Comedy*.

- My hundreds digit, tens digit, and units digit are consecutive integers, but in the reverse order to their size.
- My hundreds digit is the smallest odd prime number.
- The sum of my digits is only 7.

What year am I?

September 15

On September 15 of this year, American novelist and historian James Fenimore Cooper was born in Burlington, New Jersey. His most popular works, *The Deerslayer, The Last of the Mohicans, The Pathfinder, The Pioneers,* and *The Prairie*, feature the unique fictional character Natty Bumppo.

- My hundreds, tens, and units digits are consecutive integers whose sum is 24.

What year am I?

On September 15 of this year, William Howard Taft was born in Cincinnati, Ohio. Taft, the 27th president of the United States, was probably the heaviest U.S. president; he weighed over 225 pounds at age 20.

- My hundreds digit and tens digit are Fibonnacci numbers.
- My units digit, the largest single-digit prime is two greater than my tens digit and one less than my hundreds.

What year am I?

September 16

On September 16 of this year, Mexico's revolution against Spain began. The date is celebrated as Mexican Independence Day.

- My hundreds digit is equal to $\sqrt{64}$.
- Division by my units digit is undefined (you can't do it!).
- My thousands and tens digits are the multiplicative identity element.

What year am I?

On September 16 of this year, the Great Seal of the United States was first used by George Washington to negotiate a prisoner-of-war agreement with the British.

- My tens digit is a multiple of my units digit; it is four times the size.
- The sum of my thousands digit and my hundreds digit is equal to my tens digit.
- My hundreds and tens digits are consecutive integers whose sum is 15.

What year am I?

September 17

On September 17 of this year, the delegates from 12 states at the Constitutional Convention in Philadelphia voted to approve the Constitution of the United States.

- My hundreds, tens, and units digits form a palindrome.
- My tens digit is equal to 2^3.
- The sum of all of my digits is 23.

What year am I?

On September 17 of this year, the Battle of Antietam was fought on the banks of the Potomac River by the forces of Confederate general Robert E. Lee and Union general George McClellan. It is estimated that more than 25,000 Union and Confederate soldiers were killed or wounded in what has been called the bloodiest day in America's history.

- My hundreds, tens, and units digits are all even.
- The sum of my tens and units digits equals my hundreds digit.
- My tens digit is a perfect number.

What year am I?

September 18

On September 18 of this year, Samuel Johnson was born in Staffordshire, England. He created the first great dictionary.

- My hundreds digit is the largest one-digit prime number.
- My units digit is 3^2.
- My tens digit is the additive identity.

What year am I?

On September 18 of this year, the United States Air Force became a separate branch of the military.

- The sum of my tens digit and units digit is 11; the product is 28.
- My units digit is three greater than my tens digit.
- My hundreds digit is odd.

What year am I?

September 19

On September 19 of this year, an earthquake devastated Mexico City. There were actually two quakes: the first registering 8.2 on the Richter scale, and the second 7.5. Nearly 10,000 persons died and more than 100,000 homes were destroyed. There was more than $1 billion worth of property damage.

- My even tens and odd units digits are Fibonnacci numbers whose sum is 13 and whose product is 40.
- My hundreds digit is $\sqrt{81}$.

What year am I?

On September 19 of this year, journalist Mike Royko was born in Chicago, Illinois. His column is syndicated all over the United States.

- Both my tens digit and units digit are prime numbers; their product is 6.
- My units digit is the only even prime.
- The sum of all of my digits is 15.

What year am I?

September 20

On September 20 of this year, the Equal Rights Party was formed in San Francisco, California. Its candidate for president was Belva Lockwood, and its vice-presidential candidate was Marietta Stow.

- My tens and hundreds digits are the same cubic number.
- My units digit is $\frac{1}{2}$ my tens digit.
- My date is divisible by 2, 3, and 6.

What year am I?

On September 20 of this year, Ferdinand "Jelly Roll" Morton was born in New Orleans, Louisiana. The American jazz great was a pianist, composer, singer, and orchestra leader.

- My hundreds and tens digits are the same cubic number.
- The sum of my digits is 22.

What year am I?

September 21

On September 21 of this year, actor and comedian Bill Murray was born in Evanston, Illinois.

- My units digit is the additive identity.
- My thousands digit plus my tens digit is three less than my hundreds digit.

What year am I?

On September 21 of this year, author Stephen King was born in Portland, Maine.

- The sum of my tens digit and units digit is 11; the product is 28.
- My tens digit is an even square number.
- My hundreds digit is an odd square number.

What year am I?

September 22

On September 22 of this year, Italian immigrant Italo Marchiony applied for a patent for the ice cream cone. He had a fleet of pushcarts and sold the Italian delicacy on the streets of New York City.

- The square root of my hundreds digit is equal to my units digit.
- My tens digit is one less than my thousands digit.

What year am I?

On September 22 of this year, English scientist Michael Faraday was born. He was one of the earliest scientists to experiment with electricity.

- All of my digits are odd.
- My thousands digit and my units digit are the same.
- My tens digit is larger than my hundreds digit; their sum is 16, and their product is 63.

What year am I?

September 23

On September 23 of this year, the planet Neptune was first observed. Neptune, the eighth planet from the sun, is about 2.8 billion miles from the sun (about 30 times farther from the sun than Earth is). It takes about 165 years to revolve around the sun, and it has a diameter of about 30,000 miles (Earth's diameter is about 7,900 miles).

- All of my digits, except for my thousands digit, are even numbers.
- My hundreds digit is twice my tens; my units digit is two greater than my tens.

What year am I?

On September 23 of this year, singer and songwriter Bruce Springsteen was born in Freehold, New Jersey.

- My hundreds and units digits are the same.
- My tens digit is the square of the only even prime number.
- My hundreds, tens, and units digits form a palindrome with a sum of 22.

What year am I?

September 24

On September 24 of this year, puppeteer Jim Henson was born in Greensville, Mississippi. Among his creations were Muppets Kermit the Frog, Big Bird, Bert and Ernie, Miss Piggy, the Cookie Monster, and Oscar the Grouch.

- The sum of my tens digit and my units digit is equal to my hundreds digit.
- My prime tens digit is 50% of my perfect units digit.

What year am I?

On September 24 of this year, Babe Ruth played his last baseball game with the New York Yankees at Yankee Stadium in the Bronx, New York.

- My tens digit and units digit are consecutive integers whose product is 12.
- My date is an even number.
- The sum of my digits is 17.

What year am I?

September 25

On September 25 of this year, the first and only edition of *Publick Occurrences Both Foreign and Domestick* was published in Boston. This was the first American newspaper published, but the authorities considered it "offensive" and ordered that it be suppressed immediately.

- My hundreds digit is three less than my tens digit.
- My tens digit is equal to 3^2.
- The product of my units digit and my tens digit is the additive identity.

What year am I?

On September 25 of this year, actor Christopher Reeve was born in New York City. He played the lead in the movie *Superman*.

- Both my tens digit and my units digit are prime numbers, but my tens digit is three more than my units digit.
- The sum of my digits is 17.

What year am I?

September 26

On September 26 of this year, American composer George Gershwin was born in Brooklyn, New York. Among his songs are "The Man I Love," "Strike Up the Band," "Funny Face," and "I Got Rhythm." He also wrote the opera *Porgy and Bess*.

- My tens digit (a square number) is one more than my hundreds digit (a cubic number).
- My units digit is the same as my hundreds digit.

What year am I?

On September 26 of this year, John Chapman was born in Leominster, Massachusetts. Better known as Johnny Appleseed, he was regarded as a great medicine man by the Indians. He planted many orchards and was a friend to animals.

- My hundreds digit and tens digit are the same prime number, the largest single-digit prime.
- My units digit is an even square number.

What year am I?

September 27

On September 27 of this year, the Warren Commission issued its report, stating that Lee Harvey Oswald acted alone in the assassination of President John F. Kennedy. Sixteen years later, the House Select Committee on Assassinations issued a conflicting report, stating that there most likely was a conspiracy to kill President Kennedy.

- If my tens and units digits were the sides of a rectangle, its area would be 24 and its perimeter would be 20.
- My tens digit is a perfect number.
- The sum of my digits is 20.

What year am I?

On September 27 of this year, actor William Conrad was born in Louisville, Kentucky. He is best known for his TV roles of *Cannon* and *Jake and the Fat Man*.

- My date is divisible by 2, 3, 5, 6, and 10.
- The sum of my thousands and hundreds digits is $\frac{1}{2}$ of the two-digit number formed by my tens and units digits.

What year am I?

September 28

On September 28 of this year, the first night football game was played; teams from Mansfield University and Wyoming Seminary met in Mansfield, Pennsylvania.

- The cube root of my hundreds digit is equal to my units digit.
- My tens digit is an odd square number.

What year am I?

On September 28 of this year, American cartoonist Al Capp was born in New Haven, Connecticut. He is famous for his cartoon strip "Li'l Abner" and is the originator of Sadie Hawkins Day.

- My thousands digit times my hundreds digit is equal to my units digit.
- My tens digit is the additive identity element.
- The sum of my digits is 19.

What year am I?

September 29

On September 29 of this year London's Metropolitan Police first appeared. The police force, known as Scotland Yard, is named after the site of its first headquarters. The police officers are often called *bobbies* after the man who first organized them, Sir Robert Peel.

- The sum of my hundreds and tens digits is equal to the sum of my thousands and units digits.
- My hundreds digit is my tens digit cubed.
- The sum of all of my digits is 20.

What year am I?

On September 29 of this year, rock-and-roll star Jerry Lee Lewis was born in Ferriday, Louisiana.

- My tens digit and units digit are Fibonnacci numbers whose product is 15.
- The square root of my hundreds digit is equal to my tens digit.

What year am I?

September 30

On September 30 of this year, rioting broke out when African American James Meredith enrolled in an all-white university in Mississippi. President Kennedy sent U.S. troops to the area to ensure compliance with the law.

- My date is divisible by at least 2, 3, 6, 9 and 18.
- The sum of my tens and units digits is equal to the difference between my hundreds and thousands digits.
- My tens digit is a perfect number.

What year am I?

On September 30 of this year, the former British colony of Botswana became an independent republic.

- My tens digit and units digit are the same perfect number.
- My hundreds digit could be the area of a square with a side of 3.

What year am I?

October 1

On October 1 of this year, Babe Ruth "called his shot" in the fifth inning of Game 3 of the World Series at Wrigley Field in Chicago, Illinois. It is said that Ruth, angered by the boos of hostile Cubs fans, pointed to the center-field bleachers and hit a home run to that exact spot.

- My date is divisible by 2, 3, and 6.
- My tens digit raised to the second power is equal to my hundreds digit.
- My tens and units digits could be the sides of a rectangle with an area of 6 and a perimeter of 10.

What year am I?

On October 1 of this year, James Earl Carter was born in Plains, Georgia. The 39th president of the United States, he was responsible for the Camp David Accord—the peace treaty between Israel and Egypt. He is now very much involved in projects that help find homes for America's homeless people.

- My date is an even number.
- My units digit is 200% of my tens digit; they are consecutive even integers.
- The product of my tens and units digits is equal to the difference between my hundreds and thousands digits.

What year am I?

October 2

On October 2 of this year, Thurgood Marshall was sworn in as the first black associate justice of the U.S. Supreme Court.

- My tens digit and units digit are consecutive integers.
- My tens digit is equal to 3!.
- The sum of my digits is 23.

What year am I?

On October 2 of this year, the comic strip "Peanuts" celebrated its 41st anniversary. The comic strip, by Charles M. Schulz, now appears in 2,300 newspapers and is translated into 26 languages in 68 countries.

- I am a palindrome.
- My hundreds and tens digits are square numbers.

What year am I?

October 3

On October 3 of this year, rock-and-roll singer Chubby Checker was born in Philadelphia, Pennsylvania. His real name is Ernest Evans. His most famous song was "The Twist."

- Both my hundreds and tens digits are square numbers, but one is odd and the other is even.
- The sum of my digits is 15.

What year am I?

On October 3 of this year, the first episode of *The Andy Griffith Show* aired on TV. Every year, the 12,000-plus members of the Rerun Watchers Club meet to celebrate this date.

- The sum of my tens digit and my units digit is a perfect number.
- My units digit is the additive identity element.

What year am I?

October 4

On October 4 of this year, American author Edward Stratemeyer was born in New Jersey. He wrote the Bobbsey Twins, the Hardy Boys, and the Tom Swift books. He used more than 60 pen names and produced more than 800 books. More than 4 million copies of his books are in print.

- My hundreds digit is an even number.
- The sum of my units digit and my tens digit is equal to my hundreds digit.
- My units digit is $\sqrt{4}$.

What year am I?

On October 4 of this year, the first successful man-made satellite was launched from the U.S.S.R. It was named *Sputnik*—"fellow traveler of earth"—and its launch ushered in the Space Age.

- My tens digit and units digits are primes whose product is 35.
- My units digit is two less than my hundreds digit.

What year am I?

October 5

On October 5 of this year, Robert H. Goddard was born in Worcester, Massachusetts. Considered the "Father of the Space Age," he was ignored and ridiculed during his lifetime because of his dreams of space travel, including travel to other planets.

- My hundreds digit and tens digit are the same number.
- My units digit raised to the third power is equal to my tens digit.
- The sum of all of my digits is 19.

What year am I?

On October 5 of this year, Shawnee Indian chief and orator Tecumseh died at the Battle of the Thames. Tecumseh is regarded as one of the greatest Native Americans who worked to restore Indian lands. While he believed in peaceful methods, he did not rule out war as a last resort.

- My thousands and tens digits are the identity element for multiplication.
- My units digit is equal to $\sqrt{9}$.
- My hundreds digit is a cubic number.

What year am I?

October 6

On October 6 of this year, American inventor George Westinghouse was born.

- My hundreds, tens, and units digits are all even but none of them are the same.
- My tens digit is exactly $\frac{1}{2}$ of my hundreds digit.
- My units digit is equal to $3!$.

What year am I?

On October 6 of this year, Anwar el-Sadat was killed by assassins in Cairo, Egypt. Sadat, a Nobel Peace Prize recipient, was the president of Egypt at the time of his death. His attempt to bring peace to the Middle East by bringing the Arab states and Israel together at the peace table angered those who became his assassins.

- My thousands digit and units digit are the same.
- The sum of my tens digit and units digit is equal to my hundreds digit.
- If my tens digit were one greater, my date would be a palindrome.

What year am I?

October 7

On October 7 of this year, Ralph Wedgewood patented carbon paper. Before the invention of copiers, carbon paper was the only way to make duplicate copies of typewritten material other than having them printed.

- My hundreds, tens, and units digits are all even numbers; none of them are the same.
- My units digit is a perfect number.
- My tens digit times any number is equal to itself.
- My date is divisible by 2, 3, and 6.

What year am I?

On October 7 of this year, the first U.S. railroad opened. The tracks were made of metal so that they could be used by horse-drawn wagons.

- My tens digit is the cube root of my hundreds digit.
- My units digit is equal to 3! .

What year am I?

October 8

On October 8 of this year, the Great Chicago Fire started. According to legend, Mrs. O'Leary's cow kicked over the lantern in a barn on DeKoven Street. A large part of the city was destroyed; about 250 people died and there was about $200 million in damage to property. It is amazing that on this same date the most disastrous forest fire in history occurred in Peshtigo, Wisconsin.

- My hundreds digit is even.
- The sum of my tens digit and units digit equals my hundreds digit.
- My thousands digit and units digit are the same.

What year am I?

On October 8 of this year, civil rights leader Jesse Jackson was born in Greenville, North Carolina.

- Both my hundreds digit and my tens digit are square numbers, but one is odd and the other is even.
- If my tens digit were five greater, my date would be a palindrome.
- The sum of my digits is 15.

What year am I?

October 9

On October 9 of this year, Benjamin Banneker died in Baltimore, Maryland. Called the "First Black Man of Science," he was a man of many talents: astronomer, mathematician, clockmaker, surveyor, and author of an almanac. Banneker took part in the first survey of Washington, D.C.

- My hundreds digit is even.
- My units digit is a perfect number.
- My tens digit is the additive identity.

What year am I?

On October 9 of this year, John Lennon was born. The British singer, composer, and musician was a member of the Beatles, the rock group that became a worldwide sensation. Lennon was assassinated in New York City in 1980.

- Both my hundreds and tens digits are square numbers; one is odd and the other even.
- My date is divisible by 2, 5, and 10.
- The sum of my digits is 14.

What year am I?

October 10

On October 10 of this year, the Pledge of Allegiance to the American flag was written.

- My hundreds and tens digits are consecutive integers whose sum is 17.
- My units digit is equal to $\sqrt{4}$.
- The sum of all of my digits is 20.

What year am I?

On October 10 of this year, composer Giuseppe Verdi was born in Le Roncole, Italy. He wrote 26 operas, including *Rigoletto, Il Trovatore,* and *Aïda.*

- The two-digit number formed by my tens and units digits is the sixth prime number.
- If my thousands and hundreds digits were the sides of a rectangle, it would be long and skinny; it would have an area of 8 and a perimeter of 18.

What year am I?

October 11

On October 11 of this year, Polish-American Revolutionary War hero General Casimir Pulaski died.

- All of my digits are odd.
- My hundreds and tens digits are the same prime number; their product is 49.
- My units digit is the largest single-digit composite number.

   What year am I?

On October 11 of this year, Eleanor Roosevelt was born. The wife of President Franklin Roosevelt, she was one of America's most famous First Ladies. Among many other accomplishments, she helped to establish UNICEF. One of her famous statements was "No one can make you feel inferior without your consent."

- My hundreds and tens digits are the same cubic number.
- My units digit is half the size of my tens digit.
- My date is divisible by 2, 3, and 6.

   What year am I?

October 12

On October 12 of this year, astronaut Ronald E. McNair was born in Lake City, South Carolina. He was the second African American in space and was aboard the space shuttle *Challenger* as mission specialist when it exploded.

- My units digit is the additive identity element.
- The sum of my hundreds digit and tens digit is 14; their product is 45.

   What year am I?

On October 12 of this year, the first $10 million United States treasury note was issued.

- My hundreds digit is a cubic number and is $\sqrt{64}$.
- If my tens and units digits were the sides of a rectangle, its area would be 21.
- My units digit is one less than my hundreds digit.

   What year am I?

October 13

On October 13 of this year, Molly Pitcher (Mary Hays McCauley) was born near Trenton, New Jersey. A heroine of the American Revolution, she was known as "Sergeant Molly" after Washington made her a noncommissioned officer.

- My hundreds and tens digits are prime numbers whose sum is 12 and product is 35.
- My units digit is one less than my tens digit.
- My date is an even number.

What year am I?

On October 13 of this year, Jesse Leroy Brown was born in Hattiesburg, Mississippi. He was the first black aviator to lose his life in combat. The ship U.S.S. *Jesse L. Brown* was named in his honor.

- My date is divisible by 2, 3, 6, and 9.
- My tens digit is $\frac{1}{3}$ of my units digit; my units digit is $\frac{2}{3}$ of my hundreds digit.
- My units digit is equal to 3!.

What year am I?

October 14

On October 14 of this year, presidential candidate John F. Kennedy spoke at the University of Michigan and asked: "How many of you who are going to be doctors are willing to spend your days in Ghana? How many of you technicians and engineers are willing to work in the foreign service?" Nineteen days later he proposed the Peace Corps.

- The sum of my digits is 16.
- My tens digit is a perfect number.
- My units digit is the additive identity element.

What year am I?

On October 14 of this year, Martin Luther King, Jr., became the youngest recipient of the Nobel Peace Prize. He donated the entire prize of $54,000 to the civil rights movement.

- My tens digit is $\frac{2}{3}$ of my hundreds digit; my units digit is $\frac{2}{3}$ of my tens digit.
- The sum of my thousands and hundreds digits is equal to the sum of my tens and units digits.
- The sum of all of my digits is 20.

What year am I?

October 15

On October 15 of this year, American political activist Marty Mann was born in Chicago. She founded the National Committee for Education on Alcoholism and wrote books explaining the problems of alcoholism.

- My tens and units digits could be the sides of a square with the same perimeter and area, 16.
- The sum of my thousand, tens, and units digits is equal to my hundreds digit.

What year am I?

On October 15 of this year, Lido "Lee" Anthony Iacocca was born in Allentown, Pennsylvania. The son of Italian immigrants, he started his career as a mechanical engineer and later became an automobile executive. He was president of Ford Motor Company and later chairman of Chrysler Corporation.

- My even tens digit is the square root of my units digit.
- The sum of my thousands, tens, and units digits is two less than my hundreds digit.

What year am I?

October 16

On October 16 of this year, Noah Webster was born in West Hartford, Connecticut. Webster was an American teacher and journalist whose name became synonymous with the word "dictionary." He is responsible for compiling the first dictionary of American English.

- The sum of my thousands digit and hundreds digit is equal to my units digit.
- My units digit is equal to 2^3.
- The sum of my digits is 21.

What year am I?

On October 16 of this year, David Ben-Gurion was born in Plonsk, Poland. He was the first prime minister of the state of Israel.

- My hundreds and tens digits are the same even number.
- My units digit is $\frac{3}{4}$ of my tens digit.
- My units digit is equal to $3!$.

What year am I?

October 17

On October 17 of this year, poet Jupiter Hammon was born on Long Island, New York. He was America's first black poet, and his birth date is celebrated as Black Poetry Day. Born in slavery, Jupiter learned to read and used his master's library. With the publication of "An Evening Thought," he became the first black in America to have poetry published.

- My thousands, tens, and units digits are the same number.
- My hundreds digit is the largest single-digit prime number.

What year am I?

On October 17 of this year, the San Francisco Bay area was rocked by an earthquake that registered 7.1 on the Richter scale. It occurred just as baseball fans arrived for the World Series. The quake caused $10 billion in damage and killed 67 people, many of whom were caught in the collapse of the double-decker highway in Oakland.

- My hundreds and units digits are the same odd number.
- The sum of my thousands and tens digits is equal to my hundreds digit.

What year am I?

October 18

On October 18 of this year, the transfer of Alaska from Russia to the United States became official on Sitka's Castle Hill.

- My hundreds digit is equal to $\sqrt{64}$.
- My tens and units digits are consecutive integers whose sum is 13; their product is 42.

What year am I?

On October 18 of this year, a ruling in Canada declared women to be *persons*. Prior to this date, English common law regarded women as "persons in matters of pain and penalties, but . . . not in matters of rights and privileges." The case, brought by five women from Alberta, was led by Emily Murphy.

- The three-digit number formed by my hundreds, tens, and units digits is a palindrome with a sum of 20; two digits are odd and one is even.
- My hundreds and units digits are square numbers.
- My date is divisible by 3 but not 6.

What year am I?

October 19

On October 19 of this year, more than 7,000 English and Hessian troops led by British General Cornwallis surrendered to General George Washington at Yorktown, Virginia. This event probably ended the war between Britain and the American colonies.

- The sum of my thousands and hundreds digits is equal to my tens digit.
- My units digit is the multiplicative identity element.
- The sum of my digits is 17.

What year am I?

On October 19 of this year, world-renowned mountain climber Annie Peck was born. She climbed the Matterhorn in the Swiss Alps. She became the first American—man or woman—to climb the Peruvian peak Huascarán (22,205 feet). At the age of 61, she placed a banner saying "Votes for Women" at the top of Mount Coropuna in Peru.

- My date is divisible by 2, 5, and 10.
- My hundreds digit could be the volume of a cube with sides of 2.
- The sum of all of my digits is 14.

What year am I?

October 20

On October 20 of this year, John Dewey was born in Burlington, Vermont. He was an American psychologist, philosopher, and educational reformer.

- The sum of my thousands digit and hundreds digit is equal to my units digit.
- The product of my prime tens digit and my composite units digit is 45; their sum is 14.

What year am I?

On October 20 of this year, Christopher Wren was born. The English architect, astronomer, and mathematician is buried in the cathedral he designed: St. Paul's Cathedral in London.

- My date is divisible by 2, 3, and 6.
- The product of my tens and units digits is equal to my hundreds digit.
- My hundreds digit is equal to 3! .

What year am I?

October 21

On October 21 of this year, Thomas Alva Edison invented the first practical incandescent lamp at his laboratory in Menlo Park, New Jersey.

- My hundreds, tens, and units digits are all consecutive integers, but they're all in the wrong order.
- The sum of my hundreds and tens digits is 15; the sum of my tens digit and units digit is 16.

What year am I?

On October 21 of this year, John Birks "Dizzy" Gillespie was born in Cheraw, South Carolina. One of the founding fathers of modern jazz, he created bebop and incorporated Afro-Cuban music into jazz. When someone fell on his trumpet and bent it, Gillespie found he could hear it better, and so he left it that way.

- My thousands digit and tens digit are the multiplicative identity.
- My units digit is a prime number that is two less than my hundreds digit.

What year am I?

October 22

On October 22 of this year, President John F. Kennedy gave a nationwide address, demanding the removal of Soviet-built missiles, launching equipment, and bombers from Cuba. He set up a naval blockade; 10 days later, the U.S.S.R. agreed to remove the weapons.

- The sum of my tens, units, and thousands digits is equal to my hundreds digit.
- My units digit is $\frac{1}{3}$ the size of my tens digit.
- My tens digit is the only perfect number < 10.

What year am I?

On October 22 of this year, Annette Funicello was born in Utica, New York. Annette played one of the Mouseketeers in the original TV show, where the song beginning "M-I-C-K-E-Y-M-O-U-S-E, Mickey Mouse, Mickey Mouse . . ." became famous.

- The product of my tens digit and units digit is one less than my hundreds digit.
- My units digit is the square root of my tens digit.
- The sum of all of my digits is 16.

What year am I?

October 23

On October 23 of this year, Hungary declared itself an independent republic, 33 years after Russian troops crushed a popular revolt against Soviet rule. The elections that were held one year later were the first free elections in four decades.

- The sum of my thousands and tens digits is equal to my hundreds digit.
- My hundreds and units digits are the same odd number.
- The sum of all of my digits is 27.

What year am I?

On October 23 of this year, American swimming champion Gertrude Ederle was born in New York City. She was the first woman to swim the English Channel, and at the age of 19 she broke the previous world record by swimming the 35-mile distance in 14.5 hours.

- My units digit is $\frac{2}{3}$ of my hundreds digit.
- My tens digit is the additive identity element.
- The sum of all of my digits is 16.

What year am I?

October 24

On October 24 of this year, the New York Stock Market began its collapse after several weeks of downward trends. This day was known as "Black Thursday." Panic occurred, more than 13 million shares of stock were sold, and the nation entered more than a decade of economic depression.

- My hundreds, tens, and units digits form a palindrome with square numbers at its beginning and its end.
- The sum of all of my digits is 21.

What year am I?

On October 24 of this year, the United Nations was established. Its headquarters is located in New York City, and its purpose is to solve international problems through discussion and cooperation.

- The sum of my tens and units digits is equal to my hundreds digit.
- My date is divisible by 5.
- The two-digit number formed by my tens and units digits is a multiple of my hundreds digit.

What year am I?

October 25

On October 25 of this year, artist Pablo Picasso was born in Málaga, Spain. Considered by many to be the greatest artist of the 20th century, Picasso excelled as a painter, sculptor, and engraver. He left Spain to protest the dictatorship in that country and spent most of his life in exile in France.

- My date is a palindrome.
- The sum of all of my digits is 18.

What year am I?

On October 25 of this year, the first women to become FBI agents completed their training in Quantico, Virginia. The new agents were Susan Roley and Joanne Pierce.

- The sum of my tens and units digits is equal to my hundreds digit.
- My date is divisible by 2.
- The two-digit number formed by my tens and units digits is a multiple of my hundreds digit.
- My tens and units digits are prime numbers; if they were the sides of a rectangle, its area would be 14.

What year am I?

October 26

On October 26 of this year, American gospel singer Mahalia Jackson was born.

- My thousands, tens, and units digits are all the same number.
- My date is divisible by 3 but not 2.
- The sum of my digits is only 12.

What year am I?

On October 26 of this year, the Erie Canal was opened, providing a water route from Lake Erie to the Hudson River. This first major man-made waterway took over eight years to build and cost over $7 million. Celebrations were held all along the route for the opening, including the firing of cannons.

- All of my digits are Fibonacci numbers, but their order is not quite right.
- The sum of my tens digit and units digit is one less than my hundreds digit.
- My tens digit is the only even prime number.

What year am I?

October 27

On October 27 of this year, Theodore Roosevelt was born in New York. Roosevelt was the 26th president of the United States. He was the first president to ride in an automobile, to submerge in a submarine, and to fly in an airplane. He said, "Speak softly and carry a big stick."

- My hundreds, tens, and units digits are Fibonacci numbers; but my hundreds and units digits are the same number.
- My tens digit is three less than my units digit.

What year am I?

On October 27 of this year, the New York City subway began operation, running from City Hall to West 145th Street. It was the world's first underground *and* underwater railroad.

- Both my hundreds and units digits are square numbers, but one is odd and the other is even.
- Twice my units digit plus one is equal to my hundreds digit.
- The sum of all of my digits is 14.

What year am I?

October 28

On October 28 of this year, the Statue of Liberty was dedicated on Bedloe's Island in New York. It was sculpted by Frédéric-Auguste Bartholdi, who called it *Liberty Enlightening the World*. A sonnet by Emma Lazarus inside the pedestal of the statue contains the words, "Give me your tired, your poor, your huddled masses yearning to breathe free."

- Both my hundreds and tens digits are cubic numbers.
- The sum of all of my digits is 23.

What year am I?

On October 28 of this year, polio vaccine developer Dr. Jonas Salk was born in New York. He announced the success of the Salk vaccine a year after a polio epidemic claimed more than 3,000 lives in the United States.

- Both my hundreds and units digits are square numbers, but one is odd and the other is even.
- The product of my thousands digit and tens digit is the multiplicative identity.

What year am I?

October 29

On October 29 of this year, the National Organization for Women (NOW) was established in America. Its purpose is the liberation of both women and men.

- My tens and units digits have a sum of 12 and a product of 36.
- The sum of all of my digits is 22.

What year am I?

On October 29 of this year, political cartoonist Bill Mauldin was born in Mountain Peak, New Mexico. Perhaps his most famous cartoon was printed after the assassination of President Kennedy; it portrayed the Lincoln Monument in tears.

- My tens digit is one greater than my thousands digit.
- The two-digit number formed by my tens and units digits is a multiple of 7.
- The sum of all of my digits is 13.

What year am I?

October 30

On October 30 of this year, Orson Welles broadcast on radio an adaptation of H.G. Wells's novel *The War of the Worlds*. The radio program simulated news bulletins, and near panic resulted when some listeners believed a Martian invasion of New Jersey was really taking place.

- The sum of my thousands digit and units digit is equal to my hundreds digit.
- My tens digit is the smallest odd prime number.
- The sum of all of my digits is 21.

What year am I?

On October 30 of this year, John Adams was born in Braintree, Massachusetts. Adams, the second president of the United States, had been George Washington's vice president and was the father of John Quincy Adams, the sixth president.

- My tens and units digits are primes whose sum is 8.
- The two-digit number formed by my tens and units digits is a multiple of my hundreds digit.
- All of my digits are odd.

What year am I?

October 31

On October 31 of this year, magician and escape artist Harry Houdini (Erik Weisz) died of peritonitis following a blow to his stomach. Houdini was known for his death-defying escapes while chained underwater.

- The product of my tens and units digits is three more than my hundreds digit.
- My tens digit, $\sqrt[3]{8}$, is equal to $\frac{1}{3}$ of my units digit.

What year am I?

On October 31 of this year, the Mount Rushmore National Memorial was completed after 14 years of work. It contains the sculptures of the heads of Presidents George Washington, Thomas Jefferson, Abraham Lincoln, and Theodore Roosevelt. The 60-foot-tall sculptures represent the nation's founding, political philosophy, preservation and expansion, and conservation.

- My hundreds and tens digits are both square numbers, but one is odd and the other is even.
- The two-digit number formed by my tens and units digits is the 13th prime number.
- The sum of all of my digits is 15.

What year am I?

November 1

On November 1 of this year, Crawford Long became the first surgeon to use ether during surgery.

- My date is divisible by 7, 3, and 2.
- My tens digit is equal to half my hundreds digit.
- The sum of my digits is 15.

What year am I?

On November 1 of this year, American author Stephen Crane was born. He wrote the well-known Civil War story *The Red Badge of Courage*, but he himself never participated in a war.

- The sum of my tens digit and units digit is equal to my hundreds digit.
- My thousands digit and units digit are the same number.
- The sum of my digits is 17.

What year am I?

November 2

On November 2 of this year, American frontiersman Daniel Boone was born in Pennsylvania. Boone was captured by the Shawnee Indians and became Chief Blackfish's adopted son when he was inducted into the tribe as "Big Turtle."

- My tens and units digits are consecutive integers whose sum is equal to my hundreds digit.
- My date is divisible by 2, 3, and 6.

What year am I?

On November 2 of this year, the largest airplane ever made took its one and only flight over Long Beach Harbor in California. The 200-ton plywood craft, which cost over $25 million to build, was named the *Spruce Goose*.

- The two-digit number formed by my tens and units digits is the 15th prime number; the two-digit number formed by my thousands and hundreds digits is the 8th prime number.
- The sum of all of my digits is 21.

What year am I?

November 3

On November 3 of this year, the first national auto show was held in America. (Five years earlier, J. Frank Duryea won the first U.S. automobile race; he drove at an average speed of 7.5 mph.)

- My number is divisible by 2, 5, and 10; its sum is only 10.
- My hundreds digit is an odd square number.

What year am I?

On November 3 of this year, Stephen Austin was born in Wythe County, Virginia. The principal founder of Texas, he established a colony in Texas and was thrown in prison when he advocated the formation of a separate state; Texas still belonged to Mexico at the time. The capital city of Texas is named after him.

- My units digit is $\frac{1}{3}$ of my tens digit.
- If my hundreds digit and tens digits were the sides of a rectangle, its area would be 63 square units and its perimeter would be 32 units.

What year am I?

November 4

On November 4 of this year, Will Rogers was born in Oologah, Indian Territory (now known as Oklahoma). The American writer, actor, humorist, and grassroots philosopher was known for sayings such as "It's great to be great, but it's greater to be human."

- My hundreds digit is a Fibonacci number.
- My tens and units digits are consecutive odd numbers whose sum is 16.
- The sum of my digits is 25.

What year am I?

On November 4 of this year, actor Art Carney was born in Mt. Vernon, New York. He won an Oscar for his role in *Harry and Tonto* and many Emmys for his role in the TV show *The Honeymooners.*

- The two-digit number formed by my tens and units digits is one less than the two-digit number formed by my thousands and hundreds digits.
- The sum of all of my digits is 19.

What year am I?

November 5

On November 5 of this year, Raymond Loewy was born in Paris, France. He was an inventor, engineer, and industrial designer. His designs are evident in many areas of modern life: the U.S. Postal Service logo; the president's airplane, *Air Force One*; and automobile, train, and refrigerator designs.

- My hundreds and tens digits are consecutive integers whose sum is 17 and product is 72.
- My units digit is $\frac{1}{3}$ of my tens digit.

What year am I?

On November 5 of this year, Franklin Delano Roosevelt was elected to his third term as president of the United States.

- The sum of my thousands and hundreds digits is $\frac{1}{4}$ of the two-digit number formed by my tens and units digits.
- The sum of all of my digits is 14.

What year am I?

November 6

On November 6 of this year, American composer and band conductor John Philip Sousa was born in Washington, D.C. He is best remembered for his marches, such as "Stars and Stripes Forever" and "Semper Fidelis."

- The sum of my thousands and hundreds digits is equal to the sum of my tens and units digits.
- My tens digit is pentagonal; my units digit is square.

What year am I?

On November 6 of this year, English author Anna Sewell published *Black Beauty.*

- My thousands and units digits are the same.
- The sum of my tens digit and units digit is equal to my hundreds digit.
- My hundreds digit is an octagonal number.

What year am I?

November 7

On November 7 of this year, Jeannette Rankin was elected as the first woman to serve in the U.S. House of Representatives

- My tens and units digits, if considered a two-digit number, equal 4^2.
- The product of my tens and units digits is three less than the product of my hundreds and thousands digits.

What year am I?

On November 7 of this year, chemist and physicist Marie Curie was born in Warsaw, Poland. Working in partnership with her husband, Pierre, she isolated the element radium and, therefore, was instrumental in discovering X rays. She once made the statement "Nothing in life is to be feared; it is only to be understood."

- The sum of my odd thousands and units digits is equal to my even hundreds digit.
- My tens digit is an even triangular number.

What year am I?

November 8

On November 8 of this year, the Louvre opened to the public. One of the Paris art museum's famous paintings is the *Mona Lisa*.

- My tens digit is equal to the square of my units digit; they are both odd numbers.
- My hundreds digit is the largest single-digit prime number.

What year am I?

On November 8 of this year, English astronomer and mathematician Edmund Halley was born in London, England. He was the first to observe the comet that was named after him. Halley's Comet can be seen about every 76 years; it is next expected to be visible in 2061. There have been only 28 recorded appearances since 240 B.C.

- My hundreds and units digits are the same hexagonal number.
- The sum of my thousands digit and tens digit is equal to my hundreds digit.

What year am I?

November 9

On November 9 of this year, New York City and most of the northeastern United States blacked out due to an electric power failure. More than 30 million persons in an area of 80,000 square miles were affected.

- The sum of my thousands digit and my prime units digit is equal to my perfect tens digit.
- The product of my hundreds digit and units digit is 45.

What year am I?

On November 9 of this year, the Berlin Wall came down and the borders between East and West Berlin were opened. The wall had separated families for over 29 years and had been a symbol of the Cold War between the Soviet bloc nations and the United States.

- My hundreds and units digits are the same square number.
- The sum of my thousands digit and tens digit is equal to my hundreds digit.

What year am I?

November 10

On November 10 of this year, Americans made the first long-distance calls coast-to-coast without the assistance of an operator. This "direct dial telephone service" was inaugurated when the mayor of Englewood, New Jersey, called the mayor of Alameda, California. The call marked the beginning of a test program involving about 10,000 customers of New Jersey Bell telephone system.

- Four less than my hundreds digit is equal to my pentagonal tens digit.
- My thousands and units digits are the same number.

What year am I?

On November 10 of this year, Martin Luther was born at Eisleben, Germany. The former monk who founded Protestantism called for reformation of the Roman Catholic Church, which led to his trial for heresy and excommunication. He left the Church, married, and had six children.

- My hundreds digit is half my tens digit; both are even numbers.
- The sum of 1 and my units digit is equal to my hundreds digit.
- The sum of my digits is 16.

What year am I?

November 11

On November 11 of this year, an armistice was signed in a railway car in the Forest of Compiègne, France. Because hostilities ending this war ceased at 11 A.M., many places observe a silent memorial at the 11th hour of the 11th day of the 11th month each year.

- My thousands and tens digits are the same.
- The sum of my tens and units digits is equal to my hundreds digit.
- The sum of my digits is 19.

What year am I?

On November 11 of this year, Massachusetts passed the first law making school attendance compulsory.

- Both my hundreds and tens digits are even numbers; the tens digit is $\frac{2}{3}$ of my hundreds digit.
- My units digit minus my thousands digit is equal to my hundreds digit.
- The sum of all of my digits is 18.

What year am I?

November 12

On November 12 of this year, American woman suffragist and reformer Elizabeth Cady Stanton was born in Johnstown, New York. The 15th Amendment to the U.S. Constitution granted former male slaves the right to vote, but no *women* were allowed to vote. Women formed the National Woman Suffrage Association to achieve this right. Elizabeth Stanton became president of this group.

- My date is divisible by 3 and 5.
- My hundreds digit is equal to $2^3 \cdot$
- My thousands and tens digits are the same.

What year am I?

On November 12 of this year, French sculptor Auguste Rodin was born in Paris, France. He is best known for his statue *The Thinker*.

- My tens digit is $\frac{1}{2}$ of my hundreds digit.
- My date is divisible by 2, 5, and 10.
- The sum of my digits is 13.

What year am I?

November 13

On November 13 of this year, Scottish author Robert Louis Stevenson was born in Edinburgh, Scotland. Stevenson wrote the novels *Treasure Island, Kidnapped,* and *The Strange Case of Dr. Jekyll and Mr. Hyde*.

- The two-digit number formed by my tens and units digits is divisible by 2, 5, and 10.
- My hundreds digit is an even cubic number.
- The sum of my digits is 14.

What year am I?

On November 13 of this year, the Holland Tunnel was completed in New York. Running under the Hudson River, it connects New York City with Jersey City, New Jersey. Its two tubes accommodate two lanes of traffic.

- The sum of my tens and units digits is equal to my hundreds digit.
- If you subtracted one from my units digit and then cut that number into three equal parts, you would get my tens digit.
- The sum of all of my digits is 19.

What year am I?

November 14

On November 14 of this year, steamboat inventor Robert Fulton was born. He once stated, "Achievement is not a station in life, it is a way of traveling."

- My hundreds, tens, and units digits are consecutive integers but in reverse order.
- The three-digit number formed by my hundreds, tens, and units digits is divisible by 3 and 5.
- The two-digit number formed by my thousands and hundreds digits is a prime number.

What year am I?

On November 14 of this year, New York reporter Nellie Bly (Elizabeth Cochrane Seaman) began her attempt to repeat the fictitious voyage of Jules Verne's Phineas Fogg by traveling around the world in 80 days. She completed the trip in 72 days.

- My cubic hundreds and tens digits are one less than my units digit.
- The sum of my digits is 26.

What year am I?

November 15

On November 15 of this year, the American Federation of Labor was founded in Pittsburgh, Pennsylvania. It is now one of the largest trade unions in the United States.

- My date is a palindrome.
- The sum of my digits is 18.

What year am I?

On November 15 of this year, American artist Georgia O'Keeffe was born in Sun Prairie, Wisconsin.

- My hundreds digit and tens digit could be the sides of a square with an area of 64 square units.
- The sum of my thousands digit and units digit is equal to my tens digit.

What year am I?

November 16

On November 16 of this year, American composer W. C. Handy was born in Florence, Alabama. He was known as the "Father of the Blues."

- My hundreds digit is the sixth Fibonacci number.
- Both my tens and units digits are prime numbers whose sum is 10.
- My units digit is 5 less than my hundreds digit.

What year am I?

On November 16 of this year, Oklahoma became the 46th state of the United States.

- My units digit is equal to $\sqrt{49}$.
- My hundreds digit is equal to 3^2.
- The sum of my digits is 17.

What year am I?

November 17

On November 17 of this year, Queen Elizabeth I ascended to the throne of England.

- All of my digits are Fibonacci numbers, but only one is even.
- The sum of my prime hundreds and tens digits is 10; their product is 25.
- The sum of my thousands and units digits is one less than the sum of my tens and hundreds digits.

What year am I?

On November 17 of this year, German astronomer and mathematician August Möbius was born. He was the pioneer of topology and the first to describe the Möbius strip.

- Both my thousands and units digits are identity elements, but one is the additive identity and one is the multiplicative identity.
- My hundreds and tens digits are consecutive odd integers whose sum is 16.

What year am I?

November 18

On November 18 of this year, the squeaky-voiced Mickey Mouse first appeared on a movie screen at the Colony Theater in New York City. Walt Disney's *Steamboat Willie* was the first animated cartoon talking picture.

- My tens and units digits are Fibonacci numbers whose sum is 10 and whose product is 16.
- My tens digit is 25% of my units digit.
- The sum of all of my digits is 20.

What year am I?

On November 18 of this year, Connecticut schoolteacher Charles Dowd proposed a time-zone plan for the United States that was adopted and placed in operation. It consisted of four time zones of 15° of latitude each.

- My hundreds and tens digits are the same Fibonacci number.
- My units digit is the smallest odd prime number.
- The sum of my digits is 20.

What year am I?

November 19

On November 19 of this year, Abraham Lincoln delivered the Gettysburg Address at the ceremony dedicating 17 acres of the battlefield at Gettysburg, Pennsylvania, as a national cemetery. Though the speech took less than two minutes, it is recognized as one of the most eloquent in the English language.

- My prime units digit is $\frac{1}{2}$ of my perfect tens digit.
- My date is divisible by both 3 and 9.
- The sum of all of my digits is 18.

What year am I?

On November 19 of this year, Indira Nehru Gandhi was born. She became prime minister of India.

- My date is divisible by both 3 and 9.
- My thousands and tens digits are the same.
- My hundreds digit is a square number.

What year am I?

November 20

On November 20 of this year, New Jersey became the first state to ratify the first 10 amendments to the U.S. Constitution. These are known as our Bill of Rights.

- My hundreds, tens, and units digits are consecutive integers whose sum is 24.

What year am I?

On November 20 of this year, Chester Gould was born in Pawnee, Oklahoma. He was the creator of the comic strip "Dick Tracy," which appears in over 1,000 newspapers. Inventions that appeared in the comic strip before they appeared in real life include television, closed-circuit TV hookups, and two-way wrist radios. Some of the villains Dick Tracy triumphed over were Pruneface, Flattop, Flyface, Mole, and 88 Keys.

- My date is divisible by 2, 4, 5, and 10.
- My date is equal to 1.9×10^3.

What year am I?

November 21

On November 21 of this year, Hetty Green (Henrietta Howland Robinson Green) was born in New Bedford, Massachusetts. She was a very able financier and was reported to have been the richest woman in America. She managed her own money and was worth over $100 million.

- All of my digits are Fibonacci numbers; they are all different.
- The sum of my consecutive odd tens and units digits is equal to my hundreds digit.
- My date is divisible by 5.

What year am I?

On November 21 of this year, Harpo Marx of the Marx Brothers was born. His real name was Adolph; he was given his nickname because he played the harp.

- The sum of my thousands and hundreds digits is equal to my tens digit.
- My units digit is the square root of my tens digit.

What year am I?

November 22

On November 22 of this year, President John F. Kennedy was slain by a sniper's bullet while riding in a convertible car in Dallas, Texas. Lee Harvey Oswald, the man accused of the assassination, was killed while in police custody.

- My units digit is the square root of my hundreds digit; it is also $\frac{1}{2}$ of my tens digit.

What year am I?

On November 22 of this year, actor and comedian Rodney Dangerfield (Jacob Cohen) was born in Babylon, New York. He "just can't get no respect."

- The sum of my thousands and units digits is equal to my tens digit.
- One third of my hundreds digit minus 1 is equal to my tens digit.

What year am I?

November 23

On November 23 of this year, the first play-by-play football game was broadcast in the United States. The game, played by Texas A&M and the University of Texas, was won by Texas A&M with a score of 7–0.

- The two-digit prime number formed by my thousands and hundreds digits is the same as the two-digit prime number formed by my tens and units digits.
- If my tens and units digits were the sides of a rectangle, the perimeter would be 20 units and the area would be 9 square units.

What year am I?

On November 23 of this year, British actor Boris Karloff was born. Karloff is famous for his portrayal of monsters such as Frankenstein, Wolf Man, and Dracula.

- My hundreds and tens digits could be the sides of a square with an area of 64 and a perimeter of 32.
- The sum of my thousands and units digits is equal to my tens digit.

What year am I?

November 24

On November 24 of this year, "D.B. Cooper" bought a plane ticket on a Northwest Airlines 727 jet liner. During the flight from Portland, Oregon, to Seattle, Washington, he high-jacked the flight and collected $200,000 from the airlines. After parachuting from the plane, he disappeared and has never been apprehended.

- My date is divisible by 3 and 9.
- My thousands digit and units digit are the same.
- The two-digit number formed by my hundreds and tens digits is the largest two-digit prime number.

What year am I?

On November 24 of this year, American composer and musician Scott Joplin was born in Texarkana, Texas.

- My hundreds, tens, and units digits form a palindrome whose sum is 22.
- All of my digits (except for my thousands) are even numbers.
- My tens digit is equal to 3!.

What year am I?

November 25

On November 25 of this year, baseball player Joe DiMaggio was born in San Francisco, California. He played for the New York Yankees.

- My date is divisible by 2, 3, and 6.
- Both my hundreds and units digits are square numbers.
- My thousands and tens digits are the same Fibonacci number.

What year am I?

On November 25 of this year, the patent application for evaporated milk was submitted. Evaporated milk is unsweetened milk that has been thickened by partial evaporation; it is packaged in cans.

- My date is divisible by 2, 3, 6, and 12.
- My hundreds and tens digits are the same number; if these numbers were the sides of a square, its perimeter would be 32.
- My units digit raised to the third power is equal to the product of my hundreds and tens digits.

What year am I?

November 26

On November 26 of this year, Sojourner Truth was born in Ulster County, New York. She was one of the first American civil rights leaders. She was born a slave and changed her name (from Isabella Baumfree) when she began crusading for the abolition of slavery.

- My hundreds and tens digits are consecutive odd integers whose sum is 16.
- My units digit is six more than my thousands digit.

What year am I?

November 26 of this year was proclaimed Thanksgiving Day by President George Washington. Both houses of Congress requested him to declare a day of thanksgiving and prayer to give thanks for the opportunity to establish a form of government for the public safety and happiness.

- My hundreds, tens, and units digits are consecutive integers.
- The sum of all of my digits is 25.

What year am I?

November 27

On November 27 of this year, Anders Celsius was born. He was the Swedish astronomer who devised the Celsius or centigrade scale. We can convert Fahrenheit degrees to Celsius using the following formula:

$$\frac{(Fahrenheit° - 32) \times 5}{9} = Celsius°$$

- My date is divisible by 3 and 9 but not by 10.
- My tens digit is one less than my thousands digit.
- The sum of all of my digits is only 9.

What year am I?

On November 27 of this year, Israeli statesman Chaim Weizmann was born near Pinsk, Russia. He played an important role in bringing about the Balfour Declaration, which called for the establishment of a national home for Jews in Palestine.

- My date is divisible by 2 because my units digit is equal to 2^2.
- My hundreds and tens digits are consecutive integers but in reverse order; their sum is 15.
- My hundreds digit is twice my units digit.

What year am I?

November 28

On November 28 of this year, Lady Astor became the first woman to be elected to the British Parliament.

- I'm a somewhat boring number because the number formed by my thousands and hundreds digits is the same as the number formed by my tens and units digits.
- If my tens and units digits were the sides of a rectangle, its area would be 9 and its perimeter would be 20.

   What year am I?

On November 28 of this year, English poet and artist William Blake was born in London, England.

- My hundreds, tens, and units digits form a palindrome; all of its numbers are twin primes.
- My date is divisible by 7.
- The sum of all of my digits is 20.

   What year am I?

November 29

On November 29 of this year, American author Louisa May Alcott was born in Germantown, Pennsylvania. She is best known for her book *Little Women.*

- Four times my hundreds digit is equal to the two-digit number formed by my tens and units digits.
- My units digit is $\frac{1}{4}$ of my hundreds digit.
- The sum of all of my digits is 14.

   What year am I?

On November 29 of this year, Yugoslavia was proclaimed a republic.

- The sum of my consecutive tens and units digits is equal to my hundreds digit.
- My date is divisible by 5.

   What year am I?

November 30

On November 30 of this year, Samuel Langhorne Clemens (Mark Twain) was born in Florida, Missouri. His books include *The Adventures of Tom Sawyer*, *The Adventures of Huckleberry Finn*, and *The Prince and the Pauper*. One of his many short stories is called "The Notorious Jumping Frog of Calaveras County." Mark Twain once said, "If you tell the truth, you don't have to remember anything."

- The sum of my tens and units digits is equal to my hundreds digit.
- My tens and units digits are primes whose product is 15.
- The sum of my digits is 17.
- My date is divisible by 5.

What year am I?

On November 30 of this year, baseball and football player Bo Jackson (Vincent Edward Jackson) was born in Bessemer, Alabama.

- My hundreds digit is one more than the sum of my tens and units digits.
- My date is divisible by 2, 3, 6, and 9.
- My units digit is $\frac{1}{3}$ of my tens digit.

What year am I?

December 1

On December 1 of this year, Woody Allen (Allen Stewart Konigsburg) was born in Brooklyn, New York. He is a screen actor, writer, and producer.

- My tens and units digits are consecutive, odd primes whose sum is one less than my hundreds digit.
- The sum of my digits is 18.

What year am I?

On December 1 of this year, Rosa Parks was arrested in Montgomery, Alabama, for refusing to give up her seat and move to the back of the bus. Her arrest triggered a yearlong boycott of the city bus system and led to legal actions that ended racial segregation on municipal buses throughout the South. This event has been called the beginning of the civil rights movement in the United States.

- My tens and units digits are the same prime number; their sum is equal to the sum of my thousands and hundreds digits.

What year am I?

   730 Daily Math Warm-ups

December 2

On December 2 of this year, Russian mathematician Nicolai Ivanovich Lobachevsky was born. He changed one of Euclid's basic assumptions to say that, through a given point, *more* than one parallel line could be drawn to a given line.

- My hundreds and tens digits are consecutive odd integers whose sum is 16.
- My units digit is one more than my thousands digit.
- The sum of all of my digits is 19.

What year am I?

On December 2 of this year, President James Monroe declared that no foreign power can threaten any country in the western hemisphere.

- My tens and units digits are consecutive integers whose sum is 5.
- My hundreds digit is an octagonal number.
- The sum of all of my digits is 14.

What year am I?

December 3

On December 3 of this year, Illinois became the 21st state of the United States.

- My thousands and hundreds digits form the same two-digit number that my tens and units digits do.
- If these digits were the sides of a rectangle, its perimeter would be 18 units and its area would be 8 square units.

What year am I?

On December 3 of this year, the first heart transplant was performed at Cape Town, South Africa, by Dr. Christiaan Barnard.

- My tens and units digits are consecutive integers whose product is 42.
- The sum of all of my digits is 23.

What year am I?

December 4

On December 4 of this year, a painting in the Museum of Modern Art in New York was found to have been hung upside down. It had been in this embarrassing position for 47 days.

- My tens digit is $\frac{2}{3}$ of my hundreds digit.
- My thousands and units digits are the same number.

What year am I?

On December 4 of this year, America's first Thanksgiving was celebrated in Plymouth, Massachusetts.

- My units digit is $1\frac{1}{2}$ times the size of my hundreds digit.
- My thousands and tens digits are the multiplicative identity.
- The two-digit number formed by my tens and units digits is the eighth prime number.

What year am I?

December 5

On December 5 of this year, Wolfgang Amadeus Mozart died in Vienna, Austria. Mozart is considered one of the greatest musical geniuses of all time; he began composing at the age of 5. He wrote many successful operas, including *The Marriage of Figaro, Don Giovanni, Cosi Fan Tutti,* and *The Magic Flute.* He died when he was only 35.

- My hundreds and tens digits are consecutive odd integers; one is prime and the other is square.
- The sum of all of my digits is 18.

What year am I?

On December 5 of this year, American cartoonist Walt Disney was born.

- It is not possible to divide by my tens digit; it is *undefined*.
- My thousands and units digits are the same.
- The sum of my digits is only 11.

What year am I?

December 6

On December 6 of this year, American poet Joyce (Alfred) Kilmer was born. He is most famous for the poem "Trees," which begins, "I think that I shall never see a poem lovely as a tree . . ."

- My units digit is 75% of my tens digit.
- My hundreds digit could be the sides of a square with a perimeter of 32 and an area of 64.
- The sum of all of my digits is the ninth prime number.

What year am I?

On December 6 of this year, Ira Gershwin was born in New York. The Pulitzer Prize winner collaborated with his brother, George, to write many songs, including "Funny Face" and "Strike Up the Band."

- My hundreds and tens digits are consecutive integers whose product is 72.
- My units digit is $\frac{2}{3}$ the size of my tens digit.

What year am I?

December 7

On December 7 of this year, Delaware became the first state to join the Union.

- My hundreds, tens, and units digits form a palindrome with two odd primes and one even cubic number.
- The sum of my thousands and hundreds digits is equal to my tens digit.
- The sum of all of my digits is 23.

What year am I?

On December 7 of this year, an earthquake registering 6.9 on the Richter scale rocked the former Soviet province of Armenia, killing over 60,000 people. Many of the deaths were blamed on the poor construction of the adobelike houses.

- My tens and units digits could be the sides of a square; its perimeter would be 32 and its area would be 64.
- The sum of my thousands and hundreds digits is two greater than my tens digit.

What year am I?

December 8

On December 8 of this year, the Union of Soviet Socialist Republics ceased to exist. Russia and two other republics signed an agreement forming the Commonwealth of Independent States.

- My date is a palindrome with a sum of 20.

What year am I?

On December 8 of this year, Mexican painter Diego Rivera was born in Guanajuato, Mexico.

- My hundreds and tens digits are the same even cubic number.
- The sum of my digits is 23.

What year am I?

December 9

On December 9 of this year, Christmas Seals were first offered in the United States. This fund-raising project supports research to cure childhood illnesses.

- The product of my hundreds and units digits is 63; their sum is 16.
- My units digit is a prime number.
- The sum of the digits of my entire date is only 17.

What year am I?

On December 9 of this year, Clarence Birdseye was born in Brooklyn, New York. He was the American industrialist who developed a way of deep-freezing foods. He started by marketing frozen fish; later he was one of the founders of General Foods Corporation.

- My even hundreds and tens digits could be the sides of a square with a perimeter of 32.
- My units digit is equal to 3!.

What year am I?

December 10

On December 10 of this year, Mississippi became the 20th state to join the Union.

- The two-digit number formed by my thousands and hundreds digits is one more than the two-digit number formed by my tens and units digits.
- My thousands and hundreds digits form a composite number; my tens and units digits form a prime number.
- The sum of all of my digits is 17.

  What year am I?

On December 10 of this year, Sioux Indian chief Red Cloud died in Pine Ridge, South Dakota. A courageous leader and defender of Native American rights, he was honored by the Postal Service when it issued a stamp of him in its Great American series.

- My hundreds and units digits could be the sides of a square with a perimeter of 36.
- The sum of all of my digits is 19.

  What year am I?

December 11

On December 11 of this year, Indiana became the 19th state to join the Union.

- The two-digit numbers formed by my thousands and hundreds digits and by my tens and units digits are consecutive even integers (but they are in the reverse order).
- The two-digit number formed by my tens and units digits could be both the *perimeter* and the *area* of a square.
- My hundreds digit is a Fibonacci number.

  What year am I?

On December 11 of this year, Annie Jump Cannon was born in Dover, Delaware. She was the American astronomer who discovered five stars.

- My hundreds digit is the largest single-digit Fibonacci number.
- My tens digit is $\frac{3}{4}$ of my hundreds digit; my units digit is $\frac{1}{2}$ of my tens digit.

  What year am I?

December 12

On December 12 of this year, Pennsylvania became the second state to join the Union.

- My consecutive hundreds and tens digits could be the sides of a rectangle with a perimeter of 30 and an area of 56.
- The sum of all of my digits is 23.

What year am I?

On December 12 of this year, Frank (Francis Albert) Sinatra was born in Hoboken, New Jersey.

- My thousands and hundreds digits form a two-digit prime number; my tens and units digits form a two-digit composite that is divisible by both 3 and 5.
- The sum of all of my digits is 16.

What year am I?

December 13

On December 13 of this year, American clergyman and composer Phillips Brooks was born in Boston, Massachusetts. He is best known for writing the lyrics to "O Little Town of Bethlehem."

- My tens and units digits are twin primes whose sum is my cubic hundreds digit.
- The sum of all of my digits is 17.
- My date is divisible by 5.

What year am I?

On December 13 of this year, Mary Todd Lincoln was born in Lexington, Kentucky. She was the wife of President Lincoln.

- The two-digit number formed by my thousands and hundreds digits is the same as the two-digit number formed by my tens and units digits.
- My thousands and tens digits are the same number; my hundreds and units digits are the same number.
- My number is divisible by 2, 3, 6, and 9.

What year am I?

December 14

On December 14 of this year Roald Amundsen reached the South Pole with 4 companions and 52 sled dogs.

- The two-digit number formed by my tens and units digits is the fifth prime number.
- The sum of my digits is 12.

What year am I?

On December 14 of this year, Nostradamus was born in France. He was a physician who was best known for his prophesies. Many believe that his book actually foretold the future.

- My units digit is $\frac{1}{2}$ the sum of my thousands and hundreds digits.
- My hundreds digit is the third prime number.
- The sum of all of my digits is only 9.

What year am I?

December 15

On December 15 of this year, Alexandre Gustave Eiffel was born in Dijon, France. He was the French engineer who designed the Eiffel Tower. The tower is 1,000 feet high, is made of open-lattice wrought iron, and cost a million dollars to build. It weighs more than 7,000 tons.

- My hundreds digit is 25% of the two-digit number formed by my tens and units digits.
- The sum of my tens and units digits is 5; their product is 6.

What year am I?

On December 15 of this year, the Bill of Rights, the first 10 amendments to our Constitution, became effective following the approval of Virginia.

- My hundreds and tens digits are consecutive odd integers whose sum is 16.
- My units digit is the multiplicative identity.

What year am I?

December 16

On December 16 of this year, Ludwig van Beethoven was born in Bonn, Germany. Regarded as one of the greatest classical composers of all time, he became hearing impaired before he was 30; but even total deafness did not stop him from writing and conducting music.

- If my units digit were one greater, my date would be a palindrome.
- My units digit is the additive identity.
- The sum of my digits is 15.

What year am I?

On December 16 of this year, philosopher and writer George Santayana was born in Madrid, Spain. Santayana, who lived in the United States for many years, said, "Those who cannot remember the past are condemned to repeat it."

- My odd units digit is 50% of my even tens digit.
- My tens digit is 75% of my hundreds digit.
- The sum of my digits is 18.

What year am I?

December 17

On December 17 of this year, Orville and Wilbur Wright achieved the first documented flight of an airplane. The brothers were bicycle shop operators and wondrous inventors. The flight took place near Kitty Hawk, South Carolina, and lasted less than one minute.

- My units digit is $\frac{1}{3}$ of my hundreds digit.
- My tens digit is one less than my thousands digit.
- The sum of all of my digits is 13.

What year am I?

On December 17 of this year, the Aztec calendar was found by workmen repairing Mexico City's Central Plaza. One of the wonders of the western hemisphere, the stone is 11.5 feet in diameter and weighs nearly 25 tons. It is believed that the intricately carved calendar was made in 1479 and buried after the Spanish conquest.

- My hundreds and tens digits are consecutive odd integers whose product is 63.
- My date is divisible by 2, 5, and 10.

What year am I?

December 18

On December 18 of this year, Joseph Grimaldi was born in London, England. Called the "Greatest Clown in History" and the "King of Pantomime," he is best known for his role as "Joey the Clown."

- My hundreds and tens digits could be the sides of a square with a perimeter of 28.
- My units digit minus my thousands digit is equal to my hundreds digit.

   What year am I?

On December 18 of this year, the 13th Amendment to the U.S. Constitution was ratified. It abolished slavery.

- My date is divisible by 5 but not 10.
- Both my hundreds and tens digits are even, but my tens digit is $\frac{3}{4}$ of my hundreds digit.

   What year am I?

December 19

On December 19 of this year, *Poor Richard's Almanac* was first published. Written by Benjamin Franklin, it contains many of his witty sayings.

- The product of my odd tens digit and even units digit is one less than my prime hundreds digit.
- My date is divisible by 2 and 4.
- The sum of my digits is 13.

   What year am I?

On December 19 of this year, actress Cicely Tyson was born in New York. She received an Emmy for her performance in *The Autobiography of Miss Jane Pitman* and was nominated for an Academy Award for *Sounder*.

- My tens digit is $\frac{1}{3}$ of my hundreds digit, and my units digit is three times my tens digit.
- If my hundreds digit and units digit were the sides of a square, its perimeter would be 36.

   What year am I?

December 20

On December 20 of this year, Sacajawea died at Fort Manuel on the Missouri River. The young Shoshone Indian woman served as a guide for the Lewis and Clark expedition, which could not have succeeded without her help.

- The two-digit number formed by my thousands and hundreds digits is divisible by 2, 3, 6, and 9.
- The two-digit number formed by my tens and units digits is only divisible by 2, 3, and 4.
- The sum of all of my digits is 12.

What year am I?

On December 20 of this year, the Louisiana Purchase took place. In one of the greatest real estate deals in history, the United States purchased more than a million square miles of land from France for about $20 per square mile.

- My hundreds digit is cubic and one less than three times my units digit.
- The sum of my digits is 12.

What year am I?

December 21

On December 21 of this year, pianist Andor Foldes was born in Budapest, Hungary. He was a child prodigy who played a Mozart piano concerto with the Budapest Philharmonic when he was 8 years old.

- The two-digit numbers formed by my tens and units digits and by my thousands and hundreds digits are both prime.
- The number formed by my thousands and hundreds digits is the largest prime less than 20.
- The sum of all of my digits is 14.

What year am I?

On December 21 of this year, Henrietta Szold was born in Baltimore, Maryland. The teacher, writer, and social worker established the first night school in Baltimore, which focused on teaching English and job skills to newly arrived immigrants.

- My date is divisible by 2, 3, 5, 6, and 10.
- My hundreds digit is a cubic number; my tens digit is perfect.

What year am I?

December 22

On December 22 of this year, the first gorilla born in captivity was born at the Columbus, Ohio, zoo. It weighed 3.25 pounds at birth.

- The greatest common factor of my tens and units digits is 1; their least common multiple is 30.
- My even units digit is $\frac{2}{3}$ of my hundreds digit.
- The sum of my digits is 21.

What year am I?

On December 22 of this year, the first tube of the Lincoln Tunnel was opened. The tunnel runs underneath the Hudson River between New Jersey and New York.

- My tens and units digits form a two-digit prime number; the sum of the digits is 10.
- My units digit, the fourth prime number, is two less than my hundreds digit.
- The sum of my digits is 20.

What year am I?

December 23

On December 23 of this year, the Congress of the United States passed the Metric Conversion Act. This law declares that SI (International System of Units) will be this country's basic system of measurement, and it set up a board to oversee the planning and implementation of our conversion to the metric system.

- My tens and units digits are primes; their sum is 12.
- My hundreds digit is two greater than my tens digit.

What year am I?

On December 23 of this year, Dick Rutan and Jeana Yeager made the first nonstop flight around the world. It took 216 hours to travel the 24,986 miles at an average speed of 115 miles per hour.

- My hundreds, tens, and units digits are consecutive integers (in reverse order).
- The sum of my thousands and tens digits is equal to my hundreds digit.
- The sum of all of my digits is 25.

What year am I?

December 24

On December 24 of this year, Christopher "Kit" Carson was born in Madison County, Kentucky. Carson, an American frontiersman, was a soldier and guide.

- The sum of my thousands and hundreds digits is equal to my units digit.
- My date is divisible by 3 and 9.
- The sum of my digits is 18.

What year am I?

On December 24 of this year, Howard Hughes was born. The wealthy American recluse loved to fly and is responsible for building the *Spruce Goose*, a glider-plane with enormous wings.

- My units digit is the third prime number but the fifth Fibonacci number.
- My tens digit times any number is equal to my tens digit.
- The sum of my digits is 15.

What year am I?

December 25

On December 25 of this year, stage and screen actor Humphrey Bogart was born in New York. Among his best remembered films are *The African Queen, The Maltese Falcon,* and *Casablanca.*

- My tens and units digits could be the sides of a square with a perimeter of 36 units and an area of 81 square units.
- The sum of my thousands and hundreds digits is equal to my tens digit.

What year am I?

On December 25 of this year, Clara Barton was born in Oxford, Massachusetts. The American nurse founded the Red Cross and was the first president of the American Red Cross.

- The two-digit number formed by my tens and units digits is the eighth Fibonacci number.
- My hundreds digit is equal to $\sqrt{64}$.

What year am I?

December 26

On December 26 of this year, the Pilgrims landed at Plymouth, Massachusetts.

- My tens digit is $\frac{1}{3}$ of my hundreds digit.
- My units digit is the additive identity.
- The sum of my digits is 9.

What year am I?

On December 26 of this year, African Americans first began to observe Kwanza, a celebration of the black family. The holiday lasts seven days and consists of a community-wide harvest feast (karamu) on the seventh day. Kwanza means "first fruit" in Swahili and corresponds to African harvest festivals.

- My tens and units digits are the same; their sum is $1\frac{1}{3}$ times my hundreds digit.
- The sum of all of my digits is 22.

What year am I?

December 27

On December 27 of this year, Johannes Kepler was born in Württemberg, Germany. Kepler developed the Law of Motion of the planets and is called the "Father of Modern Astronomy."

- My hundreds and tens digits are primes whose sum is 12.
- The two-digit number formed by my hundreds and tens digits is a multiple of 19 and 3.
- The sum of all of my digits is 14.

What year am I?

On December 27 of this year, Louis Pasteur was born. The French chemist developed the treatment for rabies. The pasteurization process is named for him.

- My tens and units digits could be the sides of a square.
- My units digit, if raised to the third power, would equal my hundreds digit.
- The sum of all of my digits is 13.

What year am I?

730 Daily Math Warm-ups

December 28

On December 28 of this year, Iowa became the 29th state of the Union.

- My hundreds, tens, and units digits are all even numbers.
- My tens digit is $\frac{1}{2}$ of my hundreds digit, and my units digit is $1\frac{1}{2}$ times the size of my tens digit.
- The sum of all of my digits is 19.

What year am I?

On December 28 of this year, chewing gum was patented.

- My hundreds and tens digits are even; my units digit is odd.
- My tens digit is $\frac{2}{3}$ of my units digit; my tens digit is $\frac{3}{4}$ of my hundreds digit.
- The sum of all of my digits is 24.

What year am I?

December 29

On December 29 of this year, Texas became the 28th state to join the Union.

- My tens digit is $\frac{1}{2}$ of my hundreds digit.
- The sum of my thousands and tens digits is equal to my units digit.
- My date is divisible by 3 and 5.

What year am I?

On December 29 of this year, William Macintosh was born. He was the developer of the raincoat.

- My tens and units digits could be the sides of a square with a perimeter of 24.
- The sum of my thousands digit and tens digit is equal to my hundreds digit.
- The sum of my thousands digit and units digit is equal to my hundreds digit.

What year am I?

December 30

On December 30 of this year, baseball pitcher Sandy Koufax was born in Brooklyn, New York. Koufax was expected to pitch in a World Series game during a Jewish holiday—an act that would have violated his religion. He refused to do so and was forced to retire shortly after this incident. He became a broadcaster following his baseball career.

- My tens and units digits are prime numbers; if they were the sides of a rectangle, its perimeter would be 16.
- My tens digit is $33\frac{1}{3}\%$ of my hundreds digit.
- The sum of all of my digits is 18.

  ### What year am I?

On December 30 of this year, British writer Rudyard Kipling was born in Bombay, India. The Nobel Prize winner wrote *The Jungle Books, Just So Stories,* and *Captains Courageous.*

- My tens and units digits are consecutive integers, but in reverse order; if they were the sides of a rectangle, its perimeter would be 22.
- My hundreds digit is two more than my tens digit.
- My date is a multiple of 5.

  ### What year am I?

December 31

On December 31 of this year, the United States immigration depot opened on Ellis Island in New York.

- The sum of my thousands and hundreds digits is equal to my tens digit.
- My units digit is one less than my thousands digit.
- The sum of all of my digits is 18.

  ### What year am I?

On December 31 of this year, General Cornwallis was born. He was the British general who surrendered to George Washington, thereby ending the Revolutionary War.

- My hundreds digit is the largest single-digit prime number; my tens digit is the smallest odd prime.
- My units digit is equal to $\sqrt{64}$.

  ### What year am I?

ANSWER KEY

January Answers

January 1: Paul Revere was born in 1735; Betsy Ross was born in 1752.
January 2: The first junior high was opened in 1910; Asimov was born in 1920.
January 3: Tolkien was born in 1892; Sonya Kovalevskaya was born in 1850.
January 4: Grimm was born in 1785; Braille was born in 1809.
January 5: X rays were discovered in 1895; Ross took the oath of office in 1925.
January 6: Joan of Arc was born in 1412; Roosevelt delivered his speech in 1941.
January 7: The first election was held in 1789; the Panama Canal was opened in 1914.
January 8: Presley was born in 1935; Soupy Sales was born in 1930.
January 9: The balloon flight occurred in 1793; Balanchine was born in 1904.
January 10: Allen was born in 1738; the League of Nations was formed in 1920.
January 11: Schools were closed in 1982; Alexander Hamilton was born in 1757.
January 12: Jack London was born in 1876; Hattie Caraway was elected in 1932.
January 13: Weaver was appointed in 1966; the accordion was patented in 1854.
January 14: Albert Schweitzer was born in 1875; the Pentagon was finished in 1943.
January 15: Martin Luther King, Jr., was born in 1929; Teller was born in 1908.
January 16: The 18th Amendment was ratified in 1919; the Gulf War began in 1991.
January 17: Ben Franklin was born in 1706; Cook explored the Antarctic in 1773.
January 18: A.A. Milne was born in 1882; Roget was born in 1779.
January 19: Robert E. Lee was born in 1807; record snowfall occurred in 1881.
January 20: Medicare became law in 1966; George Burns was born in 1896.
January 21: Drivers licenses were first required by law in 1937; Clark was born in 1921.
January 22: U Thant was born in 1909; Wambaugh was born in 1937.
January 23: Elizabeth Blackwell became a doctor in 1849; John Hancock was born in 1737.
January 24: The California Gold Rush began in 1848; Tallchief was born in 1925.
January 25: Burns was born in 1759; the "Wedding March" was first played in 1858.
January 26: Franklin expressed his unhappiness in 1784; Michigan became a state in 1837.
January 27: Lewis Carroll was born in 1832; Mozart was born in 1756.
January 28: Brandeis was appointed to the Court in 1916; the shuttle exploded in 1986.
January 29: Kansas became a state in 1861; the American League was formed in 1900.
January 30: FDR was born in 1882; *The Lone Ranger* was first broadcast in 1933.
January 31: *These Are My Children* first aired in 1949; Schubert was born in 1797.

February Answers

February 1: The Supreme Court held its first session in 1790; Herbert was born in 1859.
February 2: Hallas was born in 1895; the National League was founded in 1876.
February 3: The 15th Amendment was ratified in 1870; Rockwell was born in 1894.
February 4: George Washington was named president in 1789;
the Winter Olympics were held in the United States in 1932.

February 5:	Hank Aaron was born in 1934; Stevenson was born in 1900.
February 6:	Babe Ruth was born in 1895; Reagan was born in 1911.
February 7:	Sinclair Lewis was born in 1885; Laura Ingalls Wilder was born in 1867.
February 8:	The Boy Scouts were founded in 1910; Jules Verne was born in 1828.
February 9:	The Weather Bureau was established in 1870; the earthquake occurred in 1971.
February 10:	The first singing telegram was sent in 1933; the *N.Y. Times* slogan was first printed in 1897.
February 11:	Edison was born in 1847; Japan was founded in 660 B.C.
February 12:	Lincoln was born in 1809; Bell used the telephone between cities in 1877.
February 13:	Grant Wood was born in 1892; the first magazine was published in 1747.
February 14:	Jack Benny was born in 1894; Oregon became a state in 1859.
February 15:	Galileo was born in 1564; Susan B. Anthony was born in 1820.
February 16:	King Tut's tomb was opened in 1923; Bergen was born in 1903.
February 17:	The forerunner of the PTA was formed in 1897; Michael Jordan was born in 1963.
February 18:	Shalom Aleichem was born in 1859; Tiffany was born in 1848.
February 19:	Copernicus was born in 1473; the phonograph was patented in 1878.
February 20:	Barkley was born in 1963; Glenn circled the earth in 1962.
February 21:	Lucy Hobbs graduated in 1866; Malcolm X was killed in 1965.
February 22:	George Washington was born in 1732; the leaders of the boycott were arrested in 1956.
February 23:	The U.S. flag was planted in 1945; the siege of the Alamo began in 1836.
February 24:	Grimm was born in 1786; Mexico declared its independence in 1821.
February 25:	Renoir was born in 1841; Revels was elected in 1870.
February 26:	Gleason was born in 1916; Cody was born in 1846.
February 27:	Steinbeck was born in 1902; Longfellow was born in 1807.
February 28:	The episode of *M*A*S*H* aired in 1983; Colorado was organized in 1861.
February 29:	Nemerov was born in 1920; Jack Lousma was born in 1936.

March Answers

March 1:	Yellowstone Park was established in 1872; the Peace Corps began in 1961.
March 2:	Dr. Seuss was born in 1904; school for the blind opened in 1829.
March 3:	"The Star-Spangled Banner" became our national anthem in 1931; Joyner-Kersee was born in 1962.
March 4:	The Constitution became effective in 1789; Vermont became a state in 1791.
March 5:	Ives was born in 1824; Rex Harrison was born in 1908.
March 6:	Michelangelo was born in 1475; the automobile was first driven in 1896.
March 7:	The telephone was patented in 1876; Burbank was born in 1849.
March 8:	Holmes was born in 1841; Women's Day was proclaimed in 1910.
March 9:	Vespucci was born in 1454; Howard Aiken was born in 1900.
March 10:	Tubman died in 1913; the Salvation Army was established in 1880.
March 11:	Abernathy was born in 1926; Johnny Appleseed died in 1845.
March 12:	The blizzard occurred in 1888; the parachute jump was in 1912.
March 13:	Lowell was born in 1855; Uranus was discovered in 1781.
March 14:	Einstein was born in 1879; Casey Jones was born in 1864.
March 15:	Jackson was born in 1767; Caesar was assassinated in 44 B.C.
March 16:	Madison was born in 1751; *Freedom's Journal* was published in 1827.
March 17:	Nat "King" Cole was born in 1919; Nureyev was born in 1938.
March 18:	Cleveland was born in 1837; Schick marketed the razor in 1931.

March 19:	The birds first returned in 1776; Edith Rogers was born in 1881.
March 20:	*Uncle Tom's Cabin* was published in 1852; Earth Day was first celebrated in 1979.
March 21:	Juárez was born in 1806; Pocahontas died in 1617.
March 22:	The first women's collegiate basketball game was played in 1893; Shatner was born in 1931.
March 23:	Henry gave his speech in 1775; Emmy Noether was born in 1882.
March 24:	Houdini was born in 1874; Dorothy Stratton was born in 1898.
March 25:	Gutzon Borglum was born in 1867; the fire occurred in 1911.
March 26:	Polio vaccine was introduced in 1953; Nimoy was born in 1931.
March 27:	Sarah Vaughan was born in 1924; Roentgen was born in 1845.
March 28:	The accident occurred in 1979; Raphael was born in 1483.
March 29:	Tyler was born in 1790; Pearl Bailey was born in 1918.
March 30:	Van Gogh was born in 1853; Goya was born in 1746.
March 31:	Bunsen was born in 1811; Franz Haydn was born in 1732.

April Answers

April 1:	Sophie Germain was born in 1776; Ram was born in 1908.
April 2:	Andersen was born in 1805; Bartholdi was born in 1834.
April 3:	Washington Irving was born in 1783; Hale was born in 1822.
April 4:	Dix was born in 1802; Rev. King was assassinated in 1968.
April 5:	Booker T. Washington was born in 1856; Powell was born in 1937.
April 6:	The North Pole was reached in 1909; the U.S. entered W.W. I in 1917.
April 7:	Fairchild was born in 1869; Ravi Shankar was born in 1920.
April 8:	Cushing was born in 1869; Hank Aaron set the home run record in 1974.
April 9:	The Civil War ended in 1865; Marian Anderson performed in 1939.
April 10:	Perkins was born in 1882; Robinson was recruited in 1947.
April 11:	The ASPCA began in 1866; Hughes was born in 1862.
April 12:	The big wind occurred in 1934; Letterman was born in 1947.
April 13:	Jefferson was born in 1743; the Museum of Art opened in 1870.
April 14:	Lincoln was shot in 1865; Anne Sullivan was born in 1866.
April 15:	Euler was born in 1707; Leonardo da Vinci was born in 1452.
April 16:	Wright was born in 1867; Abdul-Jabbar was born in 1947.
April 17:	Thornton Wilder was born in 1897; peace was declared in 1986.
April 18:	Paul Revere rode in 1775; the earthquake occurred in 1906.
April 19:	The Revolutionary War began in 1775; it ended in 1783.
April 20:	French was born in 1850; radium was isolated in 1902.
April 21:	Froebel was born in 1782; Charlotte Brontë was born in 1816.
April 22:	Earth Day was founded in 1970; Lenin was born in 1870.
April 23:	Shakespeare was born in 1564; Cervantes died in 1616.
April 24:	Streisand was born in 1942; the Library of Congress was established in 1800.
April 25:	The Seeing Eye dog was first used in 1923; Marconi was born in 1874.
April 26:	Richter was born in 1900; Audubon was born in 1785.
April 27:	Grant was born in 1822; Lantz was born in 1900.
April 28:	The mutiny occurred in 1789; Monroe was born in 1758.
April 29:	Hearst was born in 1863; Ellington was born in 1899.
April 30:	Gauss was born in 1777; Louisiana became a state in 1812.

May Answers

May 1:	Chardonnet was born in 1839; Mary Harris Jones was born in 1830.
May 2:	Musial broke the record in 1954; Catherine was born in 1729.
May 3:	Golda Meir was born in 1898; Robert was born in 1837.
May 4:	Mann was born in 1796; the Kent State riots occurred in 1970.
May 5:	The battle occurred in 1862; Brooks won the Pulitzer in 1950.
May 6:	Willie Mays was born in 1931; the *Hindenburg* exploded in 1937.
May 7:	Tchaikovsky was born in 1840; the *Lusitania* was sunk in 1915.
May 8:	Truman was born in 1884; de Soto reached the Mississippi River in 1541.
May 9:	The cartoon was published in 1754; the North Pole was viewed in 1926.
May 10:	The railroads were joined in 1869; the planetarium opened in 1930.
May 11:	Berlin was born in 1888; Minnesota became a state in 1858.
May 12:	Lear was born in 1812; Florence Nightingale was born in 1820.
May 13:	Jamestown was settled in 1607; Stevie Wonder was born in 1951.
May 14:	Fahrenheit was born in 1686; Israel became a nation in 1948.
May 15:	Baum was born in 1856; Ellen Church became a stewardess in 1930.
May 16:	Agnesi was born in 1718; the Oscars were first presented in 1929.
May 17:	Jenner was born in 1749; the *Brown* v. *Board of Education* ruling was in 1954.
May 18:	Mount Saint Helens erupted in 1980; Pope John Paul was born in 1920.
May 19:	Malcolm X was born in 1925; the Simplon Tunnel was opened in 1906.
May 20:	Lindbergh flew to Paris in 1927; Dolley Madison was born in 1768.
May 21:	Dürer was born in 1471; the Red Cross was founded in 1881.
May 22:	Doyle was born in 1859; Guthrie qualified for the race in 1977.
May 23:	Mesmer was born in 1734; Mansfield was born in 1846.
May 24:	The bridge opened in 1883; the first night baseball game was held in 1935.
May 25:	Sikorsky was born in 1889; Miles Davis was born in 1926.
May 26:	Sally Ride was born in 1951; John Wayne was born in 1907.
May 27:	Carson was born in 1907; the bridge was opened in 1937.
May 28:	Jim Thorpe was born in 1888; the quintuplets were born in 1934.
May 29:	John Fitzgerald Kennedy was born in 1917; Bob Hope was born in 1903.
May 30:	Mel Blanc was born in 1908; Joan of Arc died in 1431.
May 31:	Clint Eastwood was born in 1930; Walt Whitman was born in 1819.

June Answers

June 1:	Kentucky was admitted to the U.S. in 1792; the Plymouth earthquake occurred in 1638.
June 2:	Native Americans were granted citizenship in 1924; Kellerman was born in 1936.
June 3:	"Casey at the Bat" was published in 1888; Priesand was ordained in 1972.
June 4:	Marie Thible made history in 1784; King George III was born in 1738.
June 5:	Robert Kennedy was assassinated in 1968; Socrates was born in 469 B.C.
June 6:	The landing in Normandy took place in 1944; Hale was born in 1755.
June 7:	Paul Gauguin was born in 1848; Gwendolyn Brooks was born in 1917.
June 8:	Wright was born in 1867; the vacuum cleaner was patented in 1869.
June 9:	Donald Duck was "born" in 1934; Cole Porter was born in 1893.
June 10:	John Hull minted his coins in 1652; Hattie McDaniel was born in 1889.

June 11:	Jacques Cousteau was born in 1910; Jeannette Rankin was born in 1880.
June 12:	President Bush was born in 1924; Anne Frank was born in 1929.
June 13:	Evers was assassinated in 1963; Alexander the Great died in 323 B.C.
June 14:	John Bartlett was born in 1820; Harriet Beecher Stowe was born in 1811.
June 15:	Franklin conducted experiments in 1752; the Magna Carta was signed in 1215.
June 16:	John Griffen was born in 1920; Valentina Tereshkova orbited the earth in 1963.
June 17:	Battle of Bunker Hill was fought in 1775; Stravinsky was born in 1882.
June 18:	Dr. Ride went into space in 1983; Paul McCartney was born in 1942.
June 19:	Garfield was "born" in 1978; Pascal was born in 1623.
June 20:	The Great Seal was presented in 1782; Baldwin earned her degree in 1895.
June 21:	Daniel Beard was born in 1850; the wheat reaper was patented in 1834.
June 22:	The Department of Justice was established in 1870; Lindbergh was born in 1907.
June 23:	Bob Fosse was born in 1927; the first typewriter was patented in 1868.
June 24:	The Berlin Airlift began in 1949; the first UFO was sighted in 1947.
June 25:	The first color program was broadcast in 1951; George Orwell was born in 1903.
June 26:	Pearl Buck was born in 1892; the bicycle was patented in 1819.
June 27:	Keller was born in 1880; "Happy Birthday to You" was composed in 1859.
June 28:	Rubens was born in 1577; Richard Rodgers was born in 1902.
June 29:	Goethals was born in 1858; Dr. William Mayo was born in 1861.
June 30:	Charles Blondin crossed Niagara Falls in 1859; *The Guiding Light* became a soap opera in 1952.

July Answers

July 1:	The Battle of Gettysburg began in 1863; Leibniz was born in 1646.
July 2:	Thurgood Marshall was born in 1908; Dave Thomas was born in 1932.
July 3:	Idaho became a state in 1890; George M. Cohan was born in 1878.
July 4:	"America the Beautiful" was published in 1895; Foster was born in 1826.
July 5:	"Goose" Gossage was born in 1951; P.T. Barnum was born in 1810.
July 6:	Poole became a U.S. attorney in 1961; Potter was born in 1866.
July 7:	Marc Chagall was born in 1887; Ringo Starr was born in 1940.
July 8:	Eckstine was born in 1914; Count Ferdinand von Zeppelin was born in 1838.
July 9:	Elias Howe was born in 1819; the 14th Amendment was ratified in 1868.
July 10:	Mary Bethune was born in 1875; Arthur Ashe was born in 1943.
July 11:	"Day of the 5 Billion" occurred in 1987; the bridge opened in 1936.
July 12:	Buckminster Fuller was born in 1895; Thoreau was born in 1817.
July 13:	Mary Woolley was born in 1863; Harrison Ford was born in 1942.
July 14:	Isaac Bashevis Singer was born in 1904; Gerald Ford was born in 1913.
July 15:	Moore was born in 1779; St. Frances Xavier Cabrini was born in 1850.
July 16:	The earthquake hit the Philippines in 1990; Ida B. Wells was born in 1862.
July 17:	Gardner was born in 1889; "Wrong Way" Corrigan flew to Dublin in 1938.
July 18:	John Glenn was born in 1921; Nelson Mandela was born in 1918.
July 19:	Edgar Degas was born in 1834; Rosalyn Yalow was born in 1921.
July 20:	Hillary was born in 1919; Neil Armstrong stepped on the moon in 1969.
July 21:	Ernest Hemingway was born in 1899; Isaac Stern was born in 1920.
July 22:	Gregor Mendel was born in 1822; Emma Lazarus was born in 1849.
July 23:	Warner was born in 1884; Don Drysdale was born in 1936.

July 24:	Amelia Earhart was born in 1898; Alexandre Dumas was born in 1802.
July 25:	Walter Payton was born in 1954; the carousel was patented in 1871.
July 26:	George Bernard Shaw was born in 1856; Mick Jagger was born in 1943.
July 27:	The armistice was signed in 1953; the Department of State was formed in 1789.
July 28:	Jacqueline Kennedy Onassis was born in 1929; Terry Fox was born in 1958.
July 29:	Beebe was born in 1877; the *Indianapolis* was sunk in 1945.
July 30:	Henry Ford was born in 1863; Emily Brontë was born in 1818.
July 31:	The airport was dedicated in 1948; building of the U.S. Mint began in 1792.

August Answers

August 1:	Mitchell was born in 1818; Anne Frank's last entry was made in 1944.
August 2:	James Baldwin was born in 1924; L'Enfant was born in 1754.
August 3:	Otis was born in 1811; Tony Bennett was born in 1926.
August 4:	The killings took place in 1964; Wallenberg was born in 1912.
August 5:	The colony was settled in 1583; Armstrong was born in 1930.
August 6:	Lucille Ball was born in 1911; The Voting Rights Act was signed in 1965.
August 7:	Bunche was born in 1904; pictures of earth were received in 1959.
August 8:	Odie was "born" in 1978; Dustin Hoffman was born in 1937.
August 9:	Nixon resigned in 1974; Owens won in 1936.
August 10:	Missouri became a state in 1821; the Smithsonian was founded in 1846.
August 11:	Frederick Douglass spoke in 1841; Alex Haley was born in 1921.
August 12:	Cantinflas was born in 1911; Christy Mathewson was born in 1880.
August 13:	The Berlin Wall went up in 1961; Hitchcock was born in 1899.
August 14:	Thayer was born in 1863; the Social Security Act was passed in 1935.
August 15:	Bonaparte was born in 1769; Edna Ferber was born in 1887.
August 16:	Begin was born in 1913; Elvis died in 1977.
August 17:	The crossing occurred in 1978; Crockett was born in 1786.
August 18:	Dare was born in 1587; Redford was born in 1937.
August 19:	Ogden Nash was born in 1902; Roddenberry was born in 1921.
August 20:	Benjamin Harrison was born in 1833; Lovecraft was born in 1890.
August 21:	Hawaii became a state in 1959; Chamberlain was born in 1936.
August 22:	Bradbury was born in 1920; Debussy was born in 1862.
August 23:	Oliver Perry died in 1819; Gene Kelly was born in 1912.
August 24:	Vesuvius erupted in 79 A.D.; Washington burned in 1814.
August 25:	Walt Kelly was born in 1913; Bret Harte was born in 1836.
August 26:	Lavoisier was born in 1743; the 19th Amendment was ratified in 1920.
August 27:	Confucius was born 551 B.C.; Johnson was born in 1908.
August 28:	The ad was heard in 1922; Delaware Bay was discovered in 1609.
August 29:	Parker was born in 1920; Ingrid Bergman was born in 1915.
August 30:	The baby was born in 1893; Fred MacMurray was born in 1908.
August 31:	The earthquake happened in 1886; Lewis and Clark started out in 1803.

September Answers

September 1:	The plane was shot down in 1983; Nutt was hired in 1878.
September 2:	McAuliffe was born in 1948; the London fire started in 1666.
September 3:	Crandall was born in 1803; the treaty was signed in 1783.
September 4:	Burnham was born in 1846; Flaherty was hired in 1833.
September 5:	Michigan's fire started in 1881; Newhart was born in 1929.
September 6:	Rose was born in 1899; Jane Addams was born in 1860.
September 7:	Elizabeth was born in 1533; Grandma Moses was born in 1860.
September 8:	The first Miss America was crowned in 1921; *Star Trek* first aired in 1966.
September 9:	California was admitted in 1850; the Battle of Hastings took place in 1066.
September 10:	The American team was cheated out of their medal in 1972; Braxton was born in 1736.
September 11:	Tyler's cabinet resigned in 1841; O. Henry was born in 1862.
September 12:	Jesse Owens was born in 1913; *Luna 2* landed in 1959.
September 13:	New York became the seat of government in 1788; Mel Torme was born in 1925.
September 14:	Kittinger went across the Atlantic in 1984; Dante died in 1321.
September 15:	Cooper was born in 1789; Taft was born in 1857.
September 16:	Mexico's fight began in 1810; the seal was first used in 1782.
September 17:	The Constitution was approved in 1787; the battle was fought in 1862.
September 18:	Johnson was born in 1709; the Air Force was established in 1947.
September 19:	The earthquake happened in 1985; Mike Royko was born in 1932.
September 20:	The party was formed in 1884; Morton was born in 1885.
September 21:	Bill Murray was born in 1950; Stephen King was born in 1947.
September 22:	The ice cream cone was patented in 1903; Faraday was born in 1791.
September 23:	Neptune was seen in 1846; Springsteen was born in 1949.
September 24:	Jim Henson was born in 1936; Babe Ruth bid farewell in 1934.
September 25:	The newspaper was published in 1690; Reeve was born in 1952.
September 26:	Gershwin was born in 1898; Johnny Appleseed was born in 1774.
September 27:	The Warren Commission Report was published in 1964; Conrad was born in 1920.
September 28:	The football game was played in 1892; Capp was born in 1909.
September 29:	Bobbies appeared in 1829; Lewis was born in 1935.
September 30:	James Meredith enrolled in the university in 1962; Botswana became independent in 1966.

October Answers

October 1:	Babe Ruth "called his shot" in 1932; Jimmy Carter was born in 1924.
October 2:	Marshall became a justice in 1967; Charlie Brown and Snoopy celebrated their "birthday" in 1991.
October 3:	Checker was born in 1941; *The Andy Griffith Show* aired in 1960.
October 4:	Stratemeyer was born in 1862; *Sputnik* was launched in 1957.
October 5:	Robert Goddard was born in 1882; Tecumseh died in 1813.
October 6:	Westinghouse was born in 1846; Sadat was assassinated in 1981.
October 7:	Carbon paper was patented in 1806; the railroad opened in 1826.
October 8:	The fires occurred in 1871; Jesse Jackson was born in 1941.
October 9:	Banneker died in 1806; Lennon was born in 1940.
October 10:	The pledge was written in 1892; Verdi was born in 1813.

October 11:	Casimir Pulaski died in 1779; Eleanor Roosevelt was born in 1884.
October 12:	McNair was born in 1950; the note was issued in 1837.
October 13:	Molly Pitcher was born in 1754; Brown was born in 1926.
October 14:	Kennedy's speech was given in 1960; King received the prize in 1964.
October 15:	Marty Mann was born in 1944; Lee Iacocca was born in 1924.
October 16:	Noah Webster was born in 1758; Ben-Gurion was born in 1886.
October 17:	Hammon was born in 1711; the San Francisco earthquake occurred in 1989.
October 18:	Alaska was deeded to the U.S. in 1867; the ruling occurred in 1929.
October 19:	Cornwallis surrendered in 1781; Annie Peck was born in 1850.
October 20:	Dewey was born in 1859; Wren was born in 1632.
October 21:	The lightbulb was invented in 1879; Gillespie was born in 1917.
October 22:	The missile crisis took place in 1962; Funicello was born in 1942.
October 23:	Hungary became independent in 1989; Ederle was born in 1906.
October 24:	The stock market crashed in 1929; the United Nations was founded in 1945.
October 25:	Pablo Picasso was born in 1881; women joined the FBI in 1972.
October 26:	Mahalia Jackson was born in 1911; the canal was opened in 1825.
October 27:	Teddy Roosevelt was born in 1858; the subway opened in 1904.
October 28:	The statue was dedicated in 1886; Salk was born in 1914.
October 29:	NOW was established in 1966; Bill Mauldin was born in 1921.
October 30:	The show was broadcast in 1938; Adams was born in 1735.
October 31:	Harry Houdini died in 1926; Mount Rushmore was completed in 1941.

November Answers

November 1:	Crawford Long used ether in 1842; Stephen Crane was born in 1871.
November 2:	Daniel Boone was born in 1734; the *Spruce Goose* was flown in 1947.
November 3:	The auto show was held in 1900; Stephen Austin was born in 1793.
November 4:	Will Rogers was born in 1879; Art Carney was born in 1918.
November 5:	Raymond Loewy was born in 1893; Roosevelt was reelected in 1940.
November 6:	John Philip Sousa was born in 1854; Sewell published the book in 1871.
November 7:	Jeannette Rankin was elected in 1916; Marie Curie was born in 1867.
November 8:	The Louvre opened in 1793; Halley was born in 1656.
November 9:	The lights went out in 1965; the Berlin Wall came down in 1989.
November 10:	Direct-dial telephone began in 1951; Luther was born in 1483.
November 11:	Armistice was signed in 1918; school attendance became compulsory in 1647.
November 12:	Elizabeth Stanton was born in 1815; Rodin was born in 1840.
November 13:	Stevenson was born in 1850; the Holland Tunnel was completed in 1927.
November 14:	Fulton was born in 1765; Nellie Bly began her trip in 1889.
November 15:	The A.F. of L. was founded in 1881; Georgia O'Keeffe was born in 1887.
November 16:	W.C. Handy was born in 1873; Oklahoma became a state in 1907.
November 17:	Elizabeth became queen in 1558; Möbius was born in 1790.
November 18:	Mickey Mouse appeared in 1928; time zones were adopted in 1883.
November 19:	The Gettysburg Address was given in 1863; Gandhi was born in 1917.
November 20:	New Jersey ratified the Bill of Rights in 1789; Gould was born in 1900.
November 21:	Hetty Green was born in 1835; Harpo Marx was born in 1893.
November 22:	Kennedy was assassinated in 1963; Dangerfield was born in 1921.
November 23:	The football game was played in 1919; Karloff was born in 1887.

November 24:	The plane was highjacked in 1971; Scott Joplin was born in 1868.
November 25:	DiMaggio was born in 1914; evaporated milk was patented in 1884.
November 26:	Sojourner Truth was born in 1797; Thanksgiving Day was proclaimed in 1789.
November 27:	Anders Celsius was born in 1701; Chaim Weizmann was born in 1874.
November 28:	Lady Astor was elected in 1919; William Blake was born in 1757.
November 29:	Alcott was born in 1832; Yugoslavia became a republic in 1945.
November 30:	Samuel Clemens was born in 1835; Bo Jackson was born in 1962.

December Answers

December 1:	Allen was born in 1935; Rosa Parks was arrested in 1955.
December 2:	Lobachevsky was born in 1792; the Monroe Doctrine was presented in 1823.
December 3:	Illinois became a state in 1818; the heart transplant was performed in 1967.
December 4:	The painting was displayed in 1961; the first Thanksgiving was held in 1619.
December 5:	Mozart died in 1791; Disney was born in 1901.
December 6:	Joyce Kilmer was born in 1886; Ira Gershwin was born in 1896.
December 7:	Delaware became a state in 1787; the earthquake occurred in 1988.
December 8:	The U.S.S.R. ceased to exist in 1991; Diego Rivera was born in 1886.
December 9:	Christmas Seals were first sold in 1907; Birdseye was born in 1886.
December 10:	Mississippi became a state in 1817; Red Cloud died in 1909.
December 11:	Indiana became a state in 1816; Annie Cannon was born in 1863.
December 12:	Pennsylvania became a state in 1787; Frank Sinatra was born in 1915.
December 13:	Brooks was born in 1835; Mary Todd Lincoln was born in 1818.
December 14:	Amundsen reached the South Pole in 1911; Nostradamus was born in 1503.
December 15:	Eiffel was born in 1832; the Bill of Rights went into effect in 1791.
December 16:	Beethoven was born in 1770; Santayana was born in 1863.
December 17:	The flight occurred in 1903; the Aztec calendar was discovered in 1790.
December 18:	Grimaldi was born in 1778; the 13th Amendment was ratified in 1865.
December 19:	*Poor Richard's Almanac* was published in 1732; Tyson was born in 1939.
December 20:	Sacajawea died in 1812; the Louisiana Purchase was made in 1803.
December 21:	Andor Foldes was born in 1913; Henrietta Szold was born in 1860.
December 22:	The gorilla was born in 1956; the Lincoln Tunnel opened in 1937.
December 23:	The Metric Conversion Act was passed in 1975; the first nonstop flight took place in 1987.
December 24:	Kit Carson was born in 1809; Howard Hughes was born in 1905.
December 25:	Humphrey Bogart was born in 1899; Clara Barton was born in 1821.
December 26:	The Pilgrims landed in 1620; Kwanza was first celebrated in the United States in 1966.
December 27:	Kepler was born in 1571; Pasteur was born in 1822.
December 28:	Iowa became a state in 1846; chewing gum was patented in 1869.
December 29:	Texas became a state in 1845; Macintosh was born in 1766.
December 30:	Sandy Koufax was born in 1935; Rudyard Kipling was born in 1865.
December 31:	Ellis Island opened in 1890; Cornwallis was born in 1738.